TREASURES BY THE MILLIONS

The Story of The Smithsonian Institution

Books by Harry Edward Neal

Informational

TREASURES BY THE MILLIONS
The Story of The Smithsonian Institution

COMMUNICATION
From Stone Age to Space Age

SIX AGAINST CRIME
Treasury Agencies in Action

THE TELESCOPE

Career

ENGINEERS UNLIMITED
Your Career in Engineering

DISEASE DETECTIVES
Your Career in Medical Research

SKYBLAZERS
Your Career in Aviation

PATHFINDERS, U.S.A.
Your Career on Land, Sea and Air

NATURE'S GUARDIANS
Your Career in Conservation

Treasures by the Millions

the story of the Smithsonian Institution

by HARRY EDWARD NEAL

Illustrated with photographs

Julian Messner, Inc.   New York

Published by Julian Messner, Inc.

8 West 40th Street, New York 18

Published simultaneously in Canada
by The Copp Clark Publishing Co. Limited

We are grateful to the following
for the use of their photographs:

The Smithsonian Institution
MENDEL L. PETERSON
HARRY EDWARD NEAL

Printed in the United States of America
Library of Congress Catalog Card No. 61–7999

Introduction

WHEN I SET OUT TO TELL THE FASCINATING STORY OF THE Smithsonian Institution I thought it would be reasonably simple to find out what the Smithsonian is and what it does. I was wrong.

The Smithsonian I had known was a big, old, famous museum that is as much a part of America as Main Street, but I had seen it only as millions of other visitors have done. When I pried into its secrets I discovered that it is more than just a museum. It is a magic place where boys and girls can see their daydreams in plain sight and where grownups may look at yesterday under glass and enjoy happy memories of time turned back.

The Smithsonian is a house of fabulous treasures gathered from all parts of the world and brought together for the benefit of boys and girls, schoolteachers, scientists, historians, artists, and countless other people who seek to learn more about our universe.

Some of the treasures are rare jewels and works of art. Some are bugs, or stones, or fishes, or skeletons, or plants and flowers, or old steam locomotives and airplanes. Whatever they may be, they are all under the guardianship of scientists and experts whose task it is to uncover all possible information about these objects and to give this information to others who want or need it.

I was one of those who needed it so that I might write this book, and for several weeks I roamed through the halls of the Smithsonian buildings and sat in the offices and laboratories of the specialists, asking them to tell me about their treasures and their adventures. When I was finished it seemed as though I were loaded down with facts about almost everything in the world and with a lot of exciting stories about explorers and faraway places.

My profound thanks go to Dr. Leonard Carmichael, Secretary of the Smithsonian Institution, to Mr. Paul H. Oehser, Chief of its Editorial and Publications Division, and to all the curators and other people I visited, because only their generous cooperation made it possible for me to tell you this behind-the-scenes story of one of the most wonderful of all treasure troves.

I have tried to bring some of the Smithsonian to those who have never seen it—and for those who have at some time walked through its halls, I have tried to open doors to places most visitors never see.

No book, however huge, can take the place of a personal visit, and if you have never been to the Smithsonian I hope you will make plans to go, for I firmly believe that every American should see our nation's capital and the Smithsonian Institution at least once. And if you *have* visited the Smithsonian, I urge you to go again.

You'll be glad you did!

HARRY EDWARD NEAL

Contents

Chapter 1

Treasures for Twelve Million Eyes

TWO WHITE MEN STEPPED OUT OF A SMALL BOAT ON THE beach at Gonâve Island, off the mainland of Haiti, and hiked inland to the Village of the Voodoo Queen.

One was Dr. Alexander Wetmore, a renowned ornithologist; the other, Mr. Watson Perrygo, an expert taxidermist. They were from the Smithsonian Institution in Washington, D.C., and were on the island to collect various kinds of birds for their museum.

Entering the village, they were watched by scores of hostile natives, some of whom went into their thatched huts and came out with spears. The explorers halted and Dr. Wetmore spoke to a tall, muscular man who stood before a hut with arms folded.

"We come to see your Queen," Dr. Wetmore said in French.

The native shook his head. "The Queen is not here."

Slowly the other residents of the village began to encircle the white men.

"We come to hunt birds," Dr. Wetmore said. "We only want to make our headquarters in your village for a few days."

The tall man turned to his companions and held a whispered

9

conversation, then spoke again. "You pay one thousand dollars each day?"

"A thousand dollars? That's ridiculous," Perrygo said.

"That is what you pay to stay," the native answered.

In English, Dr. Wetmore said, "It's their way of saying we're not welcome."

"So what do we do now?" Perrygo asked.

Dr. Wetmore attempted to bargain with the spokesman without success. As they were about to depart he reached into his knapsack and brought out a small flashlight. He stuck the bulb end in his mouth, pushed the button and watched the natives' startled reaction as his cheeks glowed red. Then he released the button and removed the light from his mouth, whispering to Perrygo. "Now *you* do something to surprise them. Go on—do anything!"

Perrygo did the only unusual thing he could think of at the moment. He walked on his hands! The Haitians had never seen such a performance, and when Perrygo regained his feet they were so impressed by the magic light and the man who walked upside down that they broke into smiles and insisted that the explorers stay in the village free of charge. A family was evicted from its hut and the white men were ushered into their new home.

In the morning there was a great commotion because a hawk had just stolen one of the Queen's pet chickens. Perrygo saw the bird overhead, grabbed his rifle, took careful aim and fired. The hawk spiraled downward.

"The chicken was dead," Perrygo recalls, "but the Queen was happy because I had killed the hawk, and she decided that we could stay in her village as long as we pleased."

The visitors decided to move out of the thatched house, so they made a clearing near the village and put up the tent they had brought with them. They went into the jungles to shoot their bird specimens, and then returning, discovered that the villagers had erected a thatched shelter over their tent.

"Cloth no good," one native told them. "Rain water come through."

The men laughed and assured the islanders that the canvas would keep out the rain. That night it poured. "It was pretty funny," Perrygo told me. "We were in our tent and we could hear the footfalls of the villagers as they came up one by one. A hand would fumble with the tent flap and then an arm would poke through with the hand open, to see whether or not the rain was coming in!" It wasn't.

On this bird-collecting trip Watson Perrygo came closer to death than on any other trip. He had been shooting birds to be preserved and mounted, and was walking through a bamboo thicket. His native gun carrier was some distance away, hacking the jungle growth with a machete. Just as he was about to take another step Perrygo saw a snake directly in his path, coiled and ready to strike.

It was a bushmaster, one of the deadliest of all snakes. Its head was pointed at Perrygo's shins, two feet away. Perrygo stood motionless and yelled to his gun carrier to come running, but the boy evidently did not hear because of the noise of the machete. Perrygo knew that if he moved a muscle the snake would strike. It might strike anyway. This is it, he thought.

As he waited helplessly, the sweat pouring down his cheeks, he saw the bushmaster lower its head, uncoil and slither away into the brush.

The two collectors finished their mission and returned to Washington, where Watson Perrygo mounted the beautiful birds they had brought from Haiti to be placed with other feathered specimens from many parts of the world in the Natural History Museum of The Smithsonian Institution.

The Smithsonian is a kind of show window in which we may see remnants and relics of prehistoric animals and primitive men; the works and wonders of nature; the beginnings of our civilization; and the history of our own country, including the clothes worn by our ancestors, the household utensils they used, their tools, their weapons, their writing instruments— virtually everything but the living people themselves.

The original airplane built by Wilbur and Orville Wright and flown under power at Kitty Hawk, North Carolina, in 1903, shares space with the *Spirit of St. Louis,* in which Charles A. Lindbergh made the first solo nonstop flight from New York to Paris in May, 1927.

There are plaster impressions of the face and hands of Abraham Lincoln, made while he was still alive.

The original Star-Spangled Banner that waved defiantly as the British attacked Fort McHenry in 1814 is now tattered and torn, but what's left of it still hangs proudly "o'er the land of the free and the home of the brave."

In the First Ladies' Hall are several models displaying gowns worn by the wives and official hostesses of our Presidents, from Martha Washington to the First Lady of today, shown in settings patterned after the rooms in the White House, with some of the actual White House furniture.

Are you a coin or stamp collector? The Smithsonian has exceptionally fine collections of coins and stamps, including many rare issues.

Have you ever wondered what the statue on top of the United States Capitol really looks like at close range? The full-size plaster cast used to make the original figure, called the "Statue of Freedom," is at your finger tips.

Actual specimens of United States rocket missiles, including the Atlas and the Jupiter-C, stand pointing heavenward both inside and outside the buildings; but the visitor also sees the real ancestors of these giants, the rockets made by pioneer Robert H. Goddard of Clark University. Some forty years ago, when Goddard said man would one day rocket to the moon, people laughed and nicknamed him "Moony" Goddard. Today Goddard could laugh if he were alive, for his dreams have become realities.

If you're interested in power machinery there's a wonderful collection of steam, gas and oil engines, water turbines and electric generators, so arranged that you can trace the development of these machines from early times to now.

The first sewing machines, specimens of handmade lace, early American quilts and other fine needlework attract considerable attention from girls and women.

Farmers enjoy the exhibits of early plows, farm tools and farm machinery, which include the actual equipment powered at first by horses, then by steam and finally by gasoline.

Many "hot-rodders" laugh when they walk into the Transportation Hall and see the oldest automobiles in America, including the Duryea horseless carriage of 1893–94 and the pioneer Haynes and Oldsmobile, but they are surprised to learn that some of these antiques could whiz along at eighty miles an hour. Elderly visitors to this part of the Smithsonian remember when cars like these chugged down the streets of their home towns, frightening the horses. Then came Henry Ford's Model T, the famous "Tin Lizzie," which was the "poor man's automobile" and which stood up under all sorts of use and abuse. A Model T Ford stands proudly among the fancier vehicles in the Smithsonian's display.

Other forms of transportation show how our forefathers traveled many years ago. The creaking oxcart, the gleaming hansom cab, the "one-hoss shay," the old-time western stagecoach and early bicycles stand not far from the "John Bull," the oldest complete railroad locomotive in America, with other original relics and models illustrating the development of our railroads.

The Smithsonian has something about almost everything. Whether you're interested in photography, the Civil War or other wars, watches and clocks, radio and television, firearms and other weapons, calculating machines, typewriters, ships and sails, telescopes and scientific instruments, lamps and stoves, drugs and medicines, the human body and how it works, ceramics, birds, dinosaurs, insects, Indians, fossils, plants, the fine arts, music, archæology, printing and the graphic arts, meteorites, jewels or almost anything else, you will find fascinating information and displays in The Smithsonian Institution.

One of the most popular exhibits is the famous Hope diamond, the gleaming blue jewel which legend says brings evil or death to its owners.

If you enjoy watching live animals, the zoo is for you. The National Zoological Park, founded in 1890, is a part of the Smithsonian, although it is located in Rock Creek Park in Washington and is not near the Smithsonian itself. The zoo has about 2500 mammals, birds and reptiles, and welcomes more than four million visitors every year.

The National Zoological Park is only one bureau of The Smithsonian Institution. Visitors to Washington are often surprised to discover that the Smithsonian is not a one-building establishment. One building houses the Museum of Natural History. Another is called the Arts and Industries Building (Museum of History and Technology), and near it are the Air Museum and the Smithsonian Building.

The Smithsonian Building, oldest of the group, was completed about 1855 and has nine towers of various shapes, ranging from 60 to 145 feet in height. It has some graphic art exhibits, but is occupied mostly by offices.

The Arts and Industries Building, east of the Smithsonian, was originally designed to house exhibits received by the United States National Museum from the 1876 Centennial Exposition in Philadelphia. It was completed in 1881 and was the scene of the inaugural ball for President Garfield on March 4 of that year. At that time it was known as the United States National Museum, a name which still appears above the entrance. Today it houses displays in the fields of engineering and industry, medicine and public health, photography, numismatics, philately and history.

The four-story granite Natural History Building, finished in 1911, is of classic design and faces Constitution Avenue between Ninth and Twelfth streets. It has more than ten acres of floor space, occupied by exhibits of anthropology, zoology and geology; by the National Collection of Fine Arts, the Smithsonian Library, an auditorium and some administrative offices.

The Freer Gallery of Art, at Twelfth Street and Jefferson Drive, is part of the Smithsonian and lies west of the Smithsonian Building. It is built of Stony Creek granite in the style of Florentine Renaissance palace architecture. Completed in 1921, the building has two main floors. The upper floor has 18 exhibition galleries surrounding a garden court open to the sky. The lower floor has offices, study and storage rooms, a library, a photographic laboratory, workshops and an auditorium.

The Air Museum, south of the Smithsonian Building on Independence Avenue, is a hangarlike steel structure built in 1917 and was originally used as a testing laboratory for Liberty aircraft engines. It was acquired by the Smithsonian in 1919 and opened to the public in 1920.

The National Gallery of Art, opened in 1941, faces Constitution Avenue between Fourth and Seventh streets. Built at a cost exceeding 15 million dollars, it is one of the largest marble structures in the world. It is 785 feet long and has more than 500,000 square feet of floor space.

Probably few persons know that the Institution also has an Astrophysical Observatory at Cambridge, Massachusetts, and a Canal Zone Biological Area on Barro Colorado Island in the Canal Zone.

Every year more than six million persons wander through the Smithsonian's buildings on The Mall (a parklike strip extending from the Capitol to the Lincoln Memorial). Some of them merely glance at exhibits without stopping at the cases. Other visitors not only stay and study the specimens but also call on the various curators to get answers to questions on particular subjects or to work on important research projects.

The word "curator" comes from the Latin *curare*, meaning "care for," and a museum curator is responsible for the preservation, classification and maintenance of the objects and specimens under his control.

The Museum of Natural History and the Museum of History and Technology together make up the United States National Museum. The Museum of Natural History, under the direction of Dr. A. C. Smith, consists of the Departments of Anthropology, Zoology, Botany, Geology and 17 divisions of these departments.

The Museum of History and Technology, whose director is Mr. Frank A. Taylor, has the Departments of Science and Technology, Arts and Manufactures, Civil History, and Armed Forces History, comprising 15 separate divisions.

In addition, the Smithsonian has a Bureau of American Ethnology, headquarters for the study of the life and culture of the American Indian.

All of these departments, divisions and bureaus of the Smithsonian work toward "the increase and diffusion of knowledge among men." This is the wording set out in the last will and testament of the man whose money made possible the establishment of the Institution, and for whom it is named. He was James Smithson, an Englishman who had never been in the United States and who never saw The Smithsonian Institution, although his remains now lie entombed in the Smithsonian Building.

Chapter 2

The Benevolent Briton

IN 1954, WHEN QUEEN MOTHER ELIZABETH OF GREAT BRITAIN visited the United States, she asked a question of Dr. Leonard Carmichael, Secretary of the Smithsonian, which he was unable to answer.

This in itself was rather unusual, for Dr. Carmichael ordinarily could provide information about most phases of the Institution of which he has been executive officer since January 1, 1953. He could also answer questions on many other subjects. He was President of Tufts University and director of its laboratories of sensory psychology and physiology. Before that he was a faculty member at Princeton and at Brown, and dean at the University of Rochester. He is a member of the National Academy of Sciences and the American Philosophical Society, has been Chairman of the American Council on Education, and has served in several other educational posts. In other words, he has a tremendous fund of knowledge.

The question asked by the Queen Mother was a simple one about James Smithson: Why did an Englishman who never saw the United States give his fortune to establish an educational institution in this country?

The one answer Dr. Carmichael and everybody else gives to this riddle is "Nobody knows."

James Smithson was born in France in 1765, but not under

17

that name. The boy's mother, Mrs. Elizabeth Hungerford Macie, a lineal descendant of King Henry VII, had been a widow for some time before James was born. He was an illegitimate child.

Mrs. Macie brought her son to England, where he was naturalized, and in 1782 he was enrolled at Pembroke College, Oxford, as "James Lewis Macie, Gentleman Commoner." Ordinarily the entrance application required each new student to give the name of his father, but this information was not provided by James or his mother. The youth's age was given as seventeen.

At college James soon acquired a reputation as the best chemist and mineralogist in his class. He was more interested in his science studies than in recreation and sports, and in 1784 his vacation was spent in making a geological tour with a group of scientists to Oban and the Scottish western islands, where he studied mining and manufacturing processes.

James Macie graduated on May 26, 1786. In 1787 he was admitted as a Fellow of the Royal Society of London for Improving Natural Knowledge, recommended by five members as "a gentleman well versed in various branches of Natural Philosophy, and particularly in Chymistry and Mineralogy."

He was so interested in chemistry that he once captured a tear as it rolled down a lady's cheek, so that he could analyze it. There is no record to show what made the woman cry.

His first scientific paper, prepared in 1791 at his lodgings in Bentinck Street, Cavendish Square, London, was entitled *An Account of Some Chemical Experiments on Tabasheer* (a substance found in the hollow of bamboo canes) and was signed "James Lewis Macie."

It is not definitely known when he changed his name; but it was sometime before November 18, 1802, because on that date he made his second report to the Royal Society, *A Chemical Analysis of Some Calamines*, and signed it "James Smithson, Esquire."

It is possible that he had learned who his father was and took his name for two reasons: first, because the boy believed he was entitled to it and, second, because his father had died using another name.

The father, born Hugh Smithson, was a wealthy British landowner who died in 1786 when James was 21 years old. Before his death Hugh Smithson was knighted and became the Duke of Northumberland, legally changing his name to Hugh Percy. When he was buried in Westminster Abbey he was described as "the most . . . noble prince Hugh Percy, Duke and Earl of Northumberland, Earl Percy, Baron Warkworth and Lovaine, Lord Lieutenant and Custos Rotulorum of the Counties of Middlesex and Northumberland and of all America, one of the lords of His Majesty's most Honourable and Privy Council and Knight of the most noble Order of the Garter. . . . "

For some time James Smithson lived at 121 Rue Montmartre in Paris, but when he wrote his last will and testament he was again residing on Bentinck Street in London. The unusual will was made on October 23, 1826. It provided that his estate go to his nephew, Henry James Hungerford, and read:

In the case of the death of my said Nephew without leaving a child or children, I then bequeath the whole of my property . . . to the United States of America, to found at Washington, under the name of the Smithsonian Institution, an Establishment for the increase & diffusion of knowledge among men.

His reasons for his strange bequest were never explained. He had never visited America, and his papers and letters failed to show that he had ever corresponded with anyone in the United States.

James Smithson died June 27, 1829, in Genoa, Italy. His nephew died without heirs in 1835, and Smithson's estate, amounting to about $500,000—a tremendous sum in that day

—went to the United States as he had directed. The money reached America in 1838, and then the trouble began.

Some members of Congress, including fiery John C. Calhoun, protested that acceptance of the half million dollars would put the United States in the position of being a guardian for a ward, an administrator of the private estate of a foreigner. Others more farsighted, like John Quincy Adams, argued just as strongly that Smithson had made a most generous offer and that it was to the advantage of the country and to mankind to accept it.

This debate raged for eight years before Congress finally decided to take the money, and on August 10, 1846, President James K. Polk signed a bill creating an "Establishment" to be known as The Smithsonian Institution.

Under this law the Smithsonian was authorized to receive "all objects of art and foreign and curious research and objects of natural history, plants, and geological and mineral specimens belonging to the United States." The law also provided that the "minerals, books, manuscripts and other property of James Smithson, which have been received by the Government of the United States, shall be preserved separate and apart from other property of the institution."

The Establishment consisted (as it still does) of the President and Vice President of the United States, the Chief Justice and all members of the President's Cabinet. The executive officer of the Institution is the Secretary, a post equivalent to that of the head of an independent federal agency. The first Secretary was Joseph Henry, famed for his valuable discoveries in the field of electricity.

To carry out Smithson's wishes "for the increase and diffusion of knowledge among men," Joseph Henry supervised the publication of original works on various scientific subjects and their distribution to important libraries in many countries. Lectures were given in Washington; scientists were given grants of money to carry on research and to buy laboratory apparatus; and the Smithsonian began certain scientific studies to advance the work of many departments of the federal government. The United States Weather Bureau and the United States Geological Survey grew from Smithsonian activities.

Disaster came to the Smithsonian during Mr. Henry's term. In 1865 a great fire destroyed many of the Institution's specimens, including 200 of Smithson's manuscripts and thousands of his notes and memoranda. Dr. Samuel P. Langley, who later became Secretary, wrote this about the fire:

Unhappily, with the exception of one small volume, of all these nothing remains, the whole of the originals having been destroyed. . . . We know something of these manuscripts from the paper by Mr. Johnson, who had access to them before the formation of the Institution, and from it we learn that they are connected not only with science, but with history, the arts, language, rural pursuits, gardening, the construction of buildings, and kindred topics . . . while his cabinet, which was also destroyed by the fire, is described as consisting of a choice collection of minerals, comprising probably eight or ten thousand specimens in exceedingly perfect condition, including examples of most of the meteorites which had fallen in Europe during several centuries, and forming what was at the time very much the richest and rarest collection in the United States.

When Mr. Henry died in 1878 he was succeeded by Spencer Fullerton Baird, a distinguished naturalist. During Baird's term the United States was advancing its frontiers in all directions. Railroads were being built, territories were being surveyed, American explorers were heading into the Arctic and Antarctic wildernesses and the Army set up outposts in the still-wild West. All of these activities provided opportunities for the collection of rocks, plants, fossils and other specimens "for the diffusion of knowledge" by the Smithsonian, and Secretary Baird made the most of these opportunities.

Baird also developed a system for an exchange of scientific publications among many nations, an activity still carried on by the Smithsonian's International Exchange Service. In addition he invented methods for fish culture, organized the United States Fish Commission (now the Fish and Wildlife Service) and was its first Commissioner. His studies of the natural history of our waters led to the formation of the marine biological station at Woods Hole, Massachusetts, now among the foremost institutions of its kind.

The third Secretary of the Smithsonian is perhaps better known than most of the others. Samuel Pierpont Langley was a famous astronomer and inventor of the bolometer, a highly sensitive instrument for studying the sun and moon. Dr. Langley established the Astrophysical Observatory, which is still an important part of the Smithsonian.

Dr. Langley's interests were not only in the skies, for he was keenly aware that many of the larger wild animals in the United States were fast approaching extinction. To preserve the vanishing species he promoted the establishment of the National Zoological Park as a bureau of the Smithsonian Institution.

Four Secretaries followed Dr. Langley. Dr. Charles Doolittle Walcott, who served from 1907 to 1927, had been Director of the United States Geological Survey for more than 25 years. He played an important part in the establishment of the Carnegie Institution of Washington, gave advice to the President and to Congress on forest conservation and reclamation and also served as President of the National Academy of Sciences and of the American Association for the Advancement of Science.

During Dr. Walcott's term the National Collection of Fine Arts was made a separate branch of the Smithsonian, and the Freer Gallery of Art was added to the institution.

Dr. Charles Greeley Abbot was elected Secretary on January 10, 1928, after having served as Director of the Astrophysical Observatory and as Assistant Secretary. It was he who established the Division of Radiation and Organisms for the study of the effect of light on plants and animals, a division whose importance has grown with the Space Age. The National Gallery of Art was founded during Dr. Abbot's administration.

The man who followed Dr. Abbot, Dr. Alexander Wetmore, was elected Secretary on January 12, 1945. He is the man who held the flashlight in his mouth in the Village of the Voodoo Queen during his bird-collecting trip to Haiti. A famous ornithologist, Dr. Wetmore has published many papers about birds of various regions and has contributed *A Systematic Classification for the Birds of the World.*

During Dr. Wetmore's term as Secretary two bureaus were added to the Smithsonian—the National Air Museum and the Canal Zone Biological Area. Although he retired as Secretary in 1952, Dr. Wetmore was still conducting scientific studies at the Smithsonian in 1960 as a research associate.

His successor was Dr. Leonard Carmichael, mentioned at the beginning of this chapter. Dr. Carmichael injected new life into the old institution, replacing countless and formless displays in antique museum-type mahogany cases with modernized exhibits that tell enough of a story to leave a lasting impression in the mind of the casual visitor. The whole atmosphere of the Smithsonian has become new and fresh and more enjoyable than ever. It is fast becoming one of the greatest museums of the modern world, a place "for the increase and diffusion of knowledge" that James Smithson himself would praise highly if he could see it.

When Smithson died in Genoa in 1829 he was buried in a small English cemetery on the heights of San Benigno. The original inscription on his tomb carried no reference to him as the founder of the Smithsonian Institution, so the Smithsonian itself placed a tablet there to honor its founder.

In 1900 the city officials in Genoa decided to abolish the little cemetery; so in 1904 James Smithson's remains were brought to Washington, where they now lie in a tiny chapel just inside the main entrance to the Smithsonian Building.

The Smithsonian Building, erected of red-brown freestone quarried from the banks of the Chesapeake and Ohio Canal near Seneca Creek, Maryland, was designed by James Renwick, who was also the architect for St. Patrick's Cathedral and Grace Church in New York City, the original Corcoran Art Gallery (now the Court of Claims) in Washington, Vassar College, and any number of hotels, theaters, hospitals and houses in various parts of the country.

The Smithsonian Building, with its towers, spires and arched windows, resembles a true Norman castle—a fitting resting place for James Smithson, who once wrote, "The best blood of England flows in my veins . . . I am related to Kings."

Perhaps he would take even greater pride in a lighted case at the entrance to the Smithsonian's Hall of Gems and Minerals, where every year twelve million human eyes gaze at a small rock (zinc carbonate) known as "Smithsonite" in honor of Smithson's discovery of this mineral.

Chapter 3

Stone Stories

OUTER SPACE HAS BOMBARDED EARTH WITH MANY MORE MIS-siles than man has yet shot into the heavens. We call them meteorites and there is always the chance that one of them may come screaming into your back yard at any moment, for they are definitely unguided.

Millions of meteors, or "shooting stars," whiz into our atmosphere every day—thousands per minute—but most of them disintegrate in the tremendous heat of friction before they hit the ground. Those that burn and vanish are called "meteors." Those that land on the earth are "meteorites." And many do crash into our planet.

In February, 1947, a chunk of this heavenly ammunition weighing about a thousand tons slammed into the countryside of Siberia. The resulting shock wave tore 100-year-old trees into kindling and wiped an entire forest off the map. Scientists say that this unearthly flying saucer was traveling fairly slowly —only about eight miles a second—and that if its speed had been greater the damage would have been far more disastrous.

The Smithsonian and other scientific organizations are deeply interested in meteorites, especially because of man's exploration of outer space. Meteorites are the only direct messengers from the heavens that we can actually touch, and they may reveal secrets which will help to solve some of the problems of human space travel.

So far as anyone knows, no human being has ever been killed by a meteorite, although one killed a goat and some have struck houses. In 1938 a four-pounder ripped through the roof of a garage in Illinois, cut through the top of an automobile, tore through the seat cushion, struck the muffler and bounced back into the seat springs.

Perhaps the closest escape from death for humans was in 1847, when a 40-pound iron meteorite zipped into a bedroom where three children were sleeping. Although covered with debris, none of the three was injured.

I discussed meteorites with E. P. Henderson, Associate Curator of the Division of Petrology and Mineralogy in the Department of Geology at the Smithsonian, which, incidentally, has the largest meteorite collection in the United States. Of some seventeen hundred that have been recovered throughout the world, the Smithsonian has about 965. The biggest weighs about 3500 pounds, and some are no larger than a pea.

The Smithsonian's "Tucson ring meteorite," a metallic doughnut some two feet in diameter, is believed to have fallen in Muchachos, Arizona, and at one time it was set up as a public anvil in Tucson.

Meteorites are of two kinds—stone and metallic. The metallics are made of iron, nickel, cobalt and phosphorus. Contrary to popular opinion, meteorites are not hot when they land and do not start fires. If one were to whistle past your head this afternoon and slide across your front porch (and it may!) you could handle it immediately and would discover that it was lukewarm or even cold.

"The average person who thinks he has a meteorite is usually mistaken," Mr. Henderson told me. "He thinks he saw one fall close by, but this is generally an optical illusion. He goes out to hunt for it and picks up the first unusual thing he sees. Occasionally we do get a real meteorite in this manner, but we may have to sift through a thousand inquiries before we find a letter writer with the real thing."

Don't write to the Smithsonian unless you feel quite sure that your inquiry is worth time and effort. The curators have very small office staffs and, although they reply to every letter, many writers make impossible requests such as, "Please tell me everything about meteorites, satellites and Napoleon Bonaparte."

Smithsonian experts are now studying another puzzle that may be related to outer space. They have collected peculiar objects that some guess might have come from the moon! Known as *tektites*, some of these look like smooth black stones, some look like large marbles and others are about as long and as thick as a man's little finger. Held against the light, they are a dark glassy green. They are generally found in sedimentary deposits up to sixty million years old, and laboratory examination indicates that tektites were formed in temperatures much greater than known geological temperatures.

Stranger still is the fact that tektites have been found only in certain areas, including three states. One of the Smithsonian specimens came from Georgia, one from Martha's Vineyard, Massachusetts. Hundreds have been found in Texas, and many in Australia, the Philippines, China, Java and Czechoslovakia. Cave men once tipped their spears with tektites, and Australian aborigines still use them as slingshot ammunition.

If these odd fragments actually did come from the moon, they may provide us with priceless information about its physical surface, just as we have learned so much about our own planet from minerals and fossils and gems.

The prize gem in the Smithsonian collection is the famous rare, deep blue Hope diamond, so called because it was once the property of an Irish banker named Henry T. Hope, who sold it in 1906. Since that time it has had several owners, some of whom were involved in tragedies that led magazine writers to brand the Hope diamond as a messenger of disaster.

This magnificent stone is the largest of all blue diamonds,

weighing 44½ carats. At one time diamonds and other precious gems were weighed against grains or seeds, but these were so varied in size that it was necessary to standardize the carat. One metric carat is 200 milligrams, or .007 of an ounce.

The Hope diamond has a mysterious past. In August, 1792, during the French Revolution, the crown jewels of France, including certain diamonds, were stolen. One of the most precious, called the Regent, was eventually recovered. Another was a beautiful deep blue stone called "the French Blue," which weighed a little more than 67 carats and was shaped like a tear drop. The French Blue was never recovered, but in 1830, some 38 years after the theft, a large blue diamond was offered for sale in England by David Eliason, a noted gem dealer, and was bought by Henry T. Hope.

The odd fact is that the Hope diamond is slightly lopsided. Elliptical in shape, one edge is plainly less curved than the other. Some experts think that this gem was the original French Blue and that the irregularity was caused when the bottom (the tear drop) was cut away, probably so the stolen jewel could not be identified.

Two other deep blue diamonds of the same hue and quality as the Hope, although much smaller, are owned by private collectors. The weight of these two stones, together with that of the Hope diamond (allowing for a small portion lost in cutting), would equal the original weight of the French Blue.

A gift from Harry Winston, world-famous gem merchant of New York, the Hope diamond gleams in a special case and vault in the Natural History Building, where thousands of people gaze at it with mixed feelings. Some say it is too smooth and plain to be pretty, and others exclaim that it is the most magnificent jewel they have ever seen.

I asked Dr. Paul E. Desautels, Associate Curator of the Division of Mineralogy and Petrology, what specimens he would like to add to the gem collection.

"Well," he said, "we still need a good quality emerald, between fifty and one hundred carats."

In case you're interested, the *wholesale* price of such an emerald would probably be about $5000 per carat!

One spectacular exhibit in the Hall of Gems and Minerals is the world's largest crystal ball. The size of a basketball and absolutely flawless, this perfect sphere weighs 106 pounds and is probably the envy of every fortuneteller in America. The ball was cut from a block of rock crystal found in Burma and weighing more than half a ton. It was shaped in China by experts who took more than 18 months to do the job, and was presented to the Smithsonian by the widow of Worcester Reed Warner, a renowned maker of astronomical telescopes and telescope mountings.

One mineral that attracts considerable attention is the first piece of gold discovered by James W. Marshall at Sutter's Mill, California, on January 24, 1848—the nugget that sent thousands of "forty-niners" on the greatest gold rush in history. Marshall himself gave the flake of gold to the United States Army, which later presented it to the Smithsonian.

Only about five per cent of the Smithsonian's 243,000 mineral specimens are on display. The others are carefully catalogued and kept in cabinets to be made available for study to scholars, scientists and collectors.

The collection was made possible largely by private sources —especially by Washington A. Roebling, builder of the Brooklyn Bridge. A mineral collector, Roebling suffered a severe case of "the bends" during construction of the bridge, and gave up practically all activities except his collecting. He wanted to get every species of mineral, and when he died he had acquired all but twelve of the species known at that time. His entire collection was presented to the Smithsonian by his son, John, who also gave an endowment for additions to the specimens. This became the nucleus around which the institution has built its magnificent present collection.

Not all gems and minerals are gifts. Smithsonian geologists and mineralogists make field trips to get specimens out of the ground. Occasionally they are invited to visit quarries where blasting has revealed some unusual specimens. At the time of my visit they had received an invitation from the Geological Survey of the State of Georgia to go to Graves Mountain, where they are likely to find good specimens of rutile, a mineral which looks like dark brown crystals embedded in rock.

The study of objects themselves is far more fascinating than reading about them in schoolbooks, and one of the most popular "living textbooks" in the Smithsonian is its Hall of Dinosaurs. (Once when songstress Dinah Shore was visiting the Smithsonian, two teen-age girls asked a guard, "Where can we see Dinah Shore?" He sent them to the Dinosaur Hall!)

The dinosaur collection is part of the Division of Vertebrate Paleontology. A sign in the hall reads:

Paleontology is the scientific study, through fossils, of the life of past geological periods. By studying fossils we can establish a chronology of the history of the earth and learn about the course of evolution. Vertebrate paleontology is the branch of this science which deals with backboned animals. The history of backboned animals spans more than 400 million years—one of the shortest chapters in the history of life on our planet.

Fishes, amphibians, reptiles, birds and mammals are vertebrates. All other animals are invertebrates, meaning that they have no backbone.

The word "dinosaur," coined by British scientist Richard Owen in 1842, is from the Greek *deinos* ("terrible") and *sauros* ("lizard") and is the popular name for many kinds of reptiles that dominated life on earth for more than 100 million years. Scientists say that no living dinosaur was ever seen by a human being. The crocodiles and birds of today are distant relatives; but the dinosaurs have been extinct for more than

60 million years, and what we know about them has been learned only from fossils preserved in rocks.

Fossils are the remains—usually only fragments—of hard parts of the animal, such as bones and teeth. Impressions of footprints or skin have been found in ancient mud or sand, along with a few petrified dinosaur eggs. All such evidence has helped scientists to reconstruct the physical appearance of many kinds of dinosaurs and to learn much about the way they lived.

I talked with Dr. Nicholas Hotton III, Associate Curator of the Division of Vertebrate Paleontology, an expert on reptiles, including dinosaurs.

"There were very few vertebrate animals until the end of the Paleozoic era, about two hundred million years ago," he said. "The dinosaurs had their roots in the Permian period, which is an important time in vertebrate study."

"How do you find dinosaur bones?" I asked. "Or other fossils, for that matter?"

"Well, to be preserved a bone must have been in water, then buried. Finally it is buried so deeply that the mud in which it is entombed turns to rock, and it is probably several thousand feet underground. No one will find it unless it reaches the surface again or is dug out accidentally."

"But some bones are found at the surface," I said.

"Yes, because through the centuries the earth works in cycles. In what we call the cycle of emergence some fossils come close to the surface. They may lie under only four inches of earth and never be found. The paleontologist looks for exposed bone, usually in arid climates where there is no continual water flow and where the land does not slope too steeply."

Many fossils are discovered when earth is moved for road building, new housing projects and other construction work. In August, 1960, the operator of a power shovel near Langley Field, Virginia, turned up what appeared to be the bones of some giant beast. The Smithsonian was notified and Dr. Hotton and others went to investigate. They found a fossilized bowhead whale about 50 feet long. This is probably the biggest fossil of its kind ever found in the United States, and the only one found on our East Coast. The formation in which it was found was two miles inland and indicated that this whale had once roamed the waters near Norfolk, Virginia, about 15 or 20 million years ago.

The whale's skull alone weighed 450 pounds and had to be hoisted aboard a truck by the power shovel, to be taken to the Smithsonian. There it was cleaned, along with the other bones, and coated with thin plastic to be preserved for study.

Today whales are the biggest living animals; and although many dinosaurs nearly equaled them in size, other dinosaurs were no bigger than chickens. Some walked on their hind legs, some on all fours; and one group, the pterosaurs, flew like birds. Some dinosaurs ate meat, but most lived on plants.

Perhaps the most familiar example of the dinosaur is *Diplodocus*, which has a short thick body, a tapered tail, a very long neck and a small head. *Diplodocus* sometimes grew to a length of 85 feet or more and weighed ten or twelve tons. He walked on all four legs, was a vegetarian and lived in the rivers and swamps of western North America during the Upper Jurassic period, 135 million years ago.

A skeleton of *Diplodocus*, measuring about 72 feet, attracts thousands of visitors to the Dinosaur Hall in the Natural History Museum, where they also see a reconstructed armorplated *Stegosaurus* and the skeletons of other "terrible lizards." The skull of one of these, *Triceratops*, with its huge sharp horns curving upward and forward above the eyes, is about one-third the length of the animal's body and looks as fierce as any demon from a nightmare. This monster in ages past could be found roaming in Wyoming, where many of his cousins also lived.

I discussed the *Diplodocus* skeleton with F. L. Pearce,

Exhibits Specialist for the Division of Vertebrate Paleontology, who told me that the skeleton was found in 1923 in Uinta County, Utah, encased in rock. Five men worked steadily for four months to quarry out 26 tons of stone which were hauled overland by horse and wagon, crated and shipped by rail to the Smithsonian. There five men spent more than seven years to separate the dinosaur bones from the rock and to mount them for exhibition.

Because parts of some bones were missing, Smithsonian experts reconstructed them of plaster to make the skeleton complete. The plaster, however, is of a different color from the original fossils so that the spectator may readily see where the replacements were made.

Replacements of another kind took place in the earth during the centuries this skeleton lay buried. The original bone structure was gradually replaced by minerals, and by the time the fossils were discovered the transformation was complete. *Diplodocus'* pelvic bone alone weighs about one ton! So tremendous was the weight of the entire skeleton that the Smithsonian asked the Navy Department to mold and cast an iron column to support the vertebrae all the way to the skull. The Navy cast the iron at its gun factory, carried it in sections and welded it together to fit.

Mr. Pearce has been on field trips to collect specimens, mostly in the western and southwestern part of the United States.

"When you find a rock with traces of a skeleton, how do you get it out?" I asked.

"We would use light picks, hammers and chisels to chip away pieces of the rock to find the outline of the whole bone or bones," he said. "Then we cut around the surface of the ground to the depth considered necessary to get underneath the specimen. We lay strips of burlap over the top surface and cover them with plaster. We put more strips across and some around the edge for reinforcement. After the plaster sets we crack the rock or break it loose to turn it over, chip off any unnecessary material to cut down weight and cover the underside with plaster just as we did the top. Now, even if the specimen should crack, the plaster will hold it together."

The plaster-covered specimens are packed in hay or straw and placed in boxes for shipment to the Smithsonian. There Mr. Pearce and his staff will remove the plaster and the rock to expose the bone completely. To do this they may use dental burrs in a flexible shaft grinder, especially around teeth and skulls; or, for some specimens, they may coat the bone with a plastic such as polystyrene and then use formic acid to disintegrate the rock.

The job of assembling a skeleton from a pile of mixed-up fossils is not easy. The feet and teeth of mammals are the easiest bones to identify, but ribs are difficult.

"Have there been mistakes in reconstructing any missing parts?" I asked.

"Yes," he said. "Some years ago we restored a certain prehistoric reptile from a skeleton; but we had no tail bones, so we made a tail the way we thought it should be. One day a paleontologist from another city visited the museum and told us that he was familiar with this species and that the tail was wrong. We investigated and changed ours accordingly."

Fossils of several kinds have been found in many parts of the United States. In talking with Dr. D. H. Dunkle, Associate Curator of the Division of Vertebrate Paleontology, I was surprised to learn that camels, elephants and rhinoceroses once roamed the United States.

Recognizable fish were the first backboned animals to appear, according to Dr. Dunkle. They came on the scene about 400 million years ago. The first fossil fish in the Smithsonian was discovered in the Connecticut River Valley.

Dr. Dunkle, who has made field trips to Canada, Great Britain, Scandinavia, Cuba and Mexico, explained that the paleontologist must sometimes expect disappointment. "Once

I climbed a mountain, figuring that I would be the first person to visit the summit in fifty years and would find something unusual," he recalled. "I did. I found a picnic ground littered with shiny beer cans and a lot of other rubbish!"

Paleontologists who deal with invertebrate fossils have problems unlike those concerning vertebrates. Invertebrates include worms, snails, clams, oysters, starfish and other creatures without backbones. Since they consist of soft parts (except for shells), they leave no fossil bones; but sometimes they do leave impressions or stains which help to tell the story of prehistoric life.

Dr. G. A. Cooper, Head Curator of the Department of Geology, told me that fossil specimens are marked according to the level at which they are found. Each above the other is presumably younger than the one below. Sequences are worked out and matched with others in remote places to build up a history of what went on in the world's distant past.

"The Smithsonian has the most dramatic find of fossils ever made," Dr. Cooper said. "They were discovered by Dr. C. D. Walcott, fourth Secretary of the Smithsonian. In British Columbia he collected some very well-preserved slate and dug out of it several fossil animals about five hundred million years old—almost the dawn of recorded life. You can see not only their tentacles but some of their internal organs as well, and they indicate that when the Cambrian period began, about five hundred million years ago, life was already well organized."

Although much of this type of geological work may seem to have no practical value, no one can tell when certain findings may become highly important. One of the men at the Smithsonian, Dr. Joseph A. Cushman, devoted his life to a study of *foraminifera*, a tiny marine creature with a porous shell. Some foraminifera fossils were brought up in cores of earth by men making tests to find oil and drill wells. It was found that certain types of these fossils were in rock layers close to oil deposits. The oil prospectors brought core after core of earth to Dr. Cushman, who examined the fossils, if any, and identified the kind that indicated the drillers were exploring an area where oil should be found.

Geologists and paleontologists are not the only scientists interested in skulls and bones. This is a big field for the anthropologist, and one of these experts at the Smithsonian is frequently helpful to the FBI in investigating murders or other crimes involving human bones.

Chapter 4

Secrets of the Skulls and Bones

POLICE OFFICERS IN RUSSELL, KANSAS, ON NOVEMBER 14, 1957, arrested Frederick Grant Dunn as a suspected thief. Dunn was an old-time bank robber and safe burglar who frequently carried nitroglycerin with him for blowing open safe doors.

In January, 1958, Dunn escaped from jail in Lincoln, Kansas. The next night he was spotted by a policeman in Ellsworth who shot at him, but Dunn was not captured and was believed to have fled the state. Local authorities asked the FBI to help find him and in July, 1958, his name was added to the list of the "Ten Most Wanted Fugitives" issued by the FBI.

On September 8, 1959, a farmer told the sheriff at Ellsworth that he had found a skeleton and some clothing on his farm, about five miles west of town. It was believed that Dunn might have been wounded by the policeman in Ellsworth and that these might be his remains.

The skeleton, with fragments of clothing and other material found at the scene, was sent to the FBI Laboratory, where the bones were examined by Dr. T. Dale Stewart, Curator of the Division of Physical Anthropology of the Smithsonian.

Anthropology is the science dealing with the origin, development, races and customs of mankind.

The bones and a few hairs showed that the skeleton was that of a white man who had been about 5 feet 9 inches tall and was in his fifties. The nose bones slanted to the left. A copy of Dunn's health record was obtained from prison and showed that Dr. Stewart's findings were consistent with the description given. Dunn's photograph revealed that his nose twisted to the left, probably the result of an old injury he received when he was a prize fighter. A comparison of the teeth with Dunn's dental record left no doubt that the skeleton was that of Frederick Grant Dunn, whose case was then marked "Closed."

Cases of another kind develop frequently in hunting seasons. A child playing in a vacant lot or field may find what appear to be the bones of a human hand. A garbage man on the city dump may come across what he thinks is the skeleton of a human foot. Every year many police departments have excited visitors who believe they have uncovered evidence of murder, and in some cases the bones they bring in have actually (but erroneously) been identified by medical doctors as human bones, which were then forwarded to the FBI Laboratory in Washington.

The FBI seeks opinions in such cases from Dr. Stewart and his associate curator, Dr. Marshall T. Newman, and generally they establish beyond a doubt that the "hand" and "foot" bones are really those of bears! A bear's paw, with its fur and claws, is entirely unlike a man's hand; but the bones of a bear's paw are so remarkably like those of human hands and feet that only a trained anthropologist or bone specialist might readily recognize the difference.

How would the skeleton of a bear's paw get into a city dump or a vacant lot? Many hunters who kill bears skin them on the spot. Since the skin cannot easily be separated from the footpads, and because much tiresome work is necessary to skin each digit, a hunter may simply disjoint them at the wrists (front feet) or ankles (hind feet) until he gets his prize home. There, where he has more time, he skins the paws, usually leaving the end joints connected to the claws in the skin. The rest of the paw bones he throws into the garbage or some nearby field. With the claws and first joints missing, these are the "hands" and "feet" that lead so many people to believe that some foul fiend has committed some dastardly deed.

The physical anthropologist can tell a great deal by examining human bones. The more bones there are, the more he will know. If a skeleton is complete he can establish sex, height, probable weight and the approximate age at which death occurred. He can tell whether the living person was white, Negro or Mongoloid (including the American Indian) and whether he bore any distinguishing characteristics involving the bones, such as buck teeth, or a limp caused by leg-bone injury or deformity.

When an old well was cleaned out near Quantico, Virginia, a human skeleton was found at the bottom and was examined by Dr. Stewart, who concluded that it was that of a man about 25 years old who was left-handed and had suffered from pyorrhea. Later the skeleton was identified as that of a Marine 24 years and 8 months old who was left-handed and a victim of pyorrhea.

This kind of research, of course, is not typical of the work generally done in the Smithsonian's Department of Anthropology. Dr. Stewart is Acting Head Curator of this department, and under his direction are three divisions: Archaeology, Ethnology and Physical Anthropology.

The physical anthropologist has one foot in the social sciences and one in the biological sciences. He studies the origins of and differences in human populations from many parts of the world and from periods in the past. He is interested not only in variations among different races but also in learning how peoples have been affected by extremely hot or cold climates, by disease, by their geographic locations and by warfare.

The Division of Physical Anthropology makes important contributions in this field of research because it has collected some 20,000 human skulls, many with the rest of the skeleton. It also has a big collection of casts of fossil men found in parts of the Old World. As I talked with Dr. Marshall Newman in his office, we were almost surrounded with cupboards containing scores of grinning skulls and various bones. To me they were rather grisly "files," but to Dr. Newman they are simply research tools.

Research often takes the scientist to faraway and unusual places. In 1953 Dr. Ralph Solecki, then an anthropologist with the Smithsonian (now a Professor of Anthropology at Columbia University), led an expedition some 250 miles from Baghdad in northern Iraq, sponsored jointly by the Smithsonian and the Iraq government. In the valley of the Greater Zab River, north of a fertile area extending from Egypt to Iran, the scientists excavated and explored Shanidar Cave, an enormous domed chamber of rock, with the debris of centuries covering the original cave floor to a height of 45 feet. At a depth of 26 feet they unearthed the skeleton of a small child—remains which had possibly lain undisturbed for 75,000 years!

The expedition found evidence that Shanidar Cave has been almost continuously occupied by man, except for a period about 25,000 years ago when earthquakes apparently jarred some large boulders loose from the ceiling. Even today the cave serves as a winter refuge for a small group of Kurds who make homes with branches and twigs around the inside of the huge cave.

The remains of the child, consisting of the teeth, fragments of the skull and whole and partial remains of the arm and leg bones, were found near stone knives and tools of the Mousterian period of the Paleolithic Age.

In 1957 Dr. Solecki led another expedition to the cave, where he discovered three adult human skeletons, two estimated to be about 45,000 years old, the third about 60,000 years. They appeared to be Neanderthals, an extinct variety of "man-before man" identified with the last stages of the Ice Age. (Man as we know him is believed to be less than 50,000 years old—a mere blink of the geological eye.)

All three individuals had been killed by falling rocks, probably during earthquakes, and the skulls and bones were badly crushed. The right arm of one had been cut off above the elbow, probably with a stone knife, in what was perhaps one of the earliest known surgical operations. He also resembled many people of our own time in one respect—he had suffered from arthritis!

Dr. Stewart went to Baghdad in 1957 and undertook the tremendous task of piecing together the best-preserved skull, estimated to be 45,000 years old. It took three months of extraordinary knowledge, skill and precision to put together this superjigsaw puzzle, and when it was completed the scientists saw the restored skull of a unique humanlike Neanderthal creature who had been about 40 years old, about 5 feet 8 inches tall. The Neanderthalers lived in Europe, western Asia and the Near East and apparently preceded man (*Homo sapiens*) as we know him today by a few thousand years.

The Neanderthal man had most of our human features, although they were very crude. He had a massive jaw (lacking a chin), a large face, beetle brows and big teeth. He was usually a cave dweller who used stone tools.

The earliest forerunner of man is believed to be *Australopithecus* ("Southern Ape"), who lived more than half a million years ago. He was a toolmaker. Evidence indicates that this animal, which had a brain with one-third the capacity of modern man's brain, was capable of making crude tools.

The original skull restored by Dr. Stewart is in Baghdad, but a cast of the skull was given to the Smithsonian by the Iraq

Museum. Another expedition to the cave in 1960 recovered three more adult skeletons.

Dr. Stewart showed me a rib of one of the Neanderthals found in the cave. It has a slot cut into one edge, indicating that the man had been stabbed in the ribs. The bone had grown on each side of the cut, so it is likely that the blade remained in the bone for some time. No blade was found in or near the rib, and because the sides of the cut are parallel and not V-shaped, one conclusion is that the knife was made of wood which simply disintegrated with time.

Expeditions and studies such as this add to our knowledge of the evolution of man, just as ethnology provides facts about the physical distribution, the characteristics and the customs and culture of races of people.

Curator of the Division of Ethnology at the Smithsonian is Dr. S. H. Riesenberg, who has specialized in studies of the people of the Pacific islands.

The Division of Ethnology is part of the Anthropology Department and differs from the Bureau of American Ethnology, which limits its research to areas in the Americas and under American administration. Dr. Riesenberg's division has worldwide interests. He has made recent field trips to the Caroline Islands and Samoa, and is anxious to do an ethnological history of Micronesia, which includes the Marianas, Marshall, Caroline and Gilbert islands in the Pacific Ocean.

"Just how do you go about doing ethnological field work?" I asked.

Dr. Riesenberg laughed. "You sit down with the natives and talk and listen and observe. You take part in their activities to the extent possible. You might be interested in a variety of subjects, such as the political system, social organizations, folklore, music or ethnobotany (including collecting plants and studying their uses). You might be interested in the culture and personality and psychology of the people; in their fishing methods, their economic system, their ways of farming or their language and its relationship to other languages."

Dr. Riesenberg told me about some of his experiences on Ponape, a lonely, windswept island in the Caroline group. One of his major interests was native medical practices in which medicinal plants were widely used.

"On Ponape magic goes with medicine," he said. "I found great reluctance on the part of the natives to talk about it, because they believe that if they tell everything they know, they'll die. They lie in order to conceal information. Sometimes I would ask the same question of five or six different people and get five or six different answers. How can you recognize the truth? You go back in three or four months and ask the same questions and recheck your answers."

A real hot dog (the barking kind) helped the scientists in one instance. Dr. Riesenberg located one very old man whose clan had an interesting history, but when asked about it the old man said, "If I tell you everything I will die."

There is a belief on Ponape that if a dog is roasted and eaten by those who do wrong, the blame will be laid on the dog. Dr. Riesenberg and his friends got a dog (sometimes used as food on Ponape) and invited the old man to take part in the dog roast. After the man had eaten some of the meat he felt free to talk.

The Ponapeans often gave incomplete answers because of personal modesty. "Everyone is supposed to play himself down," Dr. Riesenberg told me. "If you tell a man you think he's a good carpenter he will say, 'Oh, no, I'm no good at all. Go and see John. He is much better than I.'"

This trait of self-containment brought a cruel death to one native while Dr. Riesenberg was on the island. The Ponapeans have a community house in which there is a high platform where the chiefs sit. At the other end are earthen ovens where men prepare food and kava (a native drink). The men wear "grass skirts" made of shredded hibiscus bark, and while one man was tending an oven a red-hot coal set fire to his skirt.

"The man knew it, of course," Dr. Riesenberg said, "but it was beneath him to try to put out the fire or to call attention to it. He would simply have to wait silently until someone else noticed it and extinguished it, because it would be cowardly to do anything else. By the time others came to his rescue it was too late. He died from the burns."

The ideal man of Ponape sits alert in his house, talks very little, sleeps very little, does not laugh much and is always pre- pared to fight. Each day he gets up before dawn and hikes to his secret yam fields high in the hills. He cultivates his yams and after sunrise goes back to his house.

"Yams are not raised primarily for food, but for prestige," Dr. Riesenberg said. "The way to get a title of distinction is to present the chief with the largest yam of all, and this is the principal reason for keeping secret the location of the yam fields. If you present the chief with a new kind of yam, you're made! On the other hand, a man may know that he has the biggest yam in creation; but his modesty compels him to deny it. The yam, of course, speaks for itself."

Ponape yams are not like our sweet-potato variety. Dr. Riesenberg saw one weighing about 200 pounds, called a "four-man yam" because it took four men to carry it slung between two poles. "That was a small one," Dr. Riesenberg recalled. "I learned about one twenty-man yam that had to be carried on a litter."

The Division of Ethnology has thousands of specimens in its research collection. From Micronesia, for instance, there are two fishing kites from Ifalik. The kites are flown at sea by natives in canoes. Dangling from each kite line is a ball made of cobwebs which are of a sticky substance, used for catching garfish. The ball bobs around on the waves until a garfish strikes. When he takes a bite he can't open his mouth because it is glued shut by the cobwebs, and the fisherman hauls him in!

The division receives numerous inquiries from people everywhere. The Post Office Department wants to borrow an Alaskan dog sled used in bygone days for mail deliveries. A scholar in Los Angeles wants photographs of 180 masks of Eskimos. An educational organization on the West Coast is preparing a western history show and wants to use various Indian weapons, pottery, costumes and other historical items. A man from Iowa sends in a sword that belonged to his grandfather. Where did it come from? A girl forwards a wood carving that her father picked up in West Africa. What tribe made it?

Similar questions come to the Division of Archaeology, headed by Dr. Waldo R. Wedel.

Most people don't like to have others dig up their past, but this is actually the purpose of the archaeologist—digging up the past to study the activities of mankind. "Archaeology" is derived from Greek words meaning "ancient study," and experts in this field have already uncovered scores of buried cities and evidences of old civilizations that tell us fascinating stories of vanished peoples and how they lived.

Archaeology is also useful in more unusual ways. During World War II the Japanese sent up balloons with incendiary bombs, designed to be blown across the Pacific and to set fires along the West Coast of the United States. Some of the balloons landed without exploding the bombs. A Smithsonian archaeologist examined some of the sand which had stuck to the balloons and pinpointed the Japanese area from which they were launched, and which then became a target for American bombers.

If you are interested in ancient Egypt you can visualize the way its people lived through scores of specimens in the Hall of Archaeology. Besides mummy cases and their once-human contents, you see two mummified Egyptian bulls and a mummified cat and kitten.

In Ancient Egypt the cat was sacred to Bast, the Sky Goddess. A magnificent temple in her honor was built at Bubastis, the center of Bast worship, and close by was a cat cemetery. When a cat died, all occupants of the house went into mourning. The body was embalmed, bandaged in linen and buried in a bronze or wooden case. The Smithsonian's mummified cat and kitten look like two long, thick, cloth-covered clubs somewhat thicker than baseball bats. No legs or other body shapes are visible, but the animals' heads stick out at the top.

Close by are cases with reproductions of skulls of the Neanderthal man and the Java man, who lived in Java during the first interglacial period almost a million years ago.

Smithsonian displays include many life-size figures of Indians, Eskimos and peoples from other countries. The facial features of most of these are authentic because they were made from life masks. A life mask (or a death mask) is made by covering a person's face with plaster or a plastic composition, thus producing a mold from which an exact replica of the features may be made.

Frank Setzler, who retired in 1960 as Head Curator of Anthropology, went to Australia in 1948 as a member of a Smithsonian–National Geographic expedition and made life masks of aborigines in Arnhem Land. Mr. A. Joseph Andrews, Chief Exhibits Preparator for the Department of Anthropology, told me that in 1960 he made several life masks of Koreans, Samoans and Pakistanians which will be used to produce authentic features of these nationalities in Smithsonian displays. As models he used volunteers employed in Washington by the embassies of the various countries.

Archaeologists have made unusual discoveries in our own country. Dr. Wedel showed me two small heavily encrusted fragments in which faint circular outlines could still be seen. "We think these are pieces of ancient chain mail," he said. "They were dug up along with bits of armor at a site in central

Kansas that had been regarded locally as the destination of Coronado's expedition in 1541."

The Smithsonian's primary purpose was to find out whether or not the site did belong to that period, as local historians believed.

The iron had been completely rusted away, but the ring shape remained and there were enough specimens so that experts from the Metropolitan Museum of New York, who also took part, were satisfied that these were pieces of chain mail. When clean and shiny the links might have been used by the Indians to make necklaces or bracelets.

"Chain mail was on the way out in the sixteenth century, so it isn't likely that these pieces came from expeditions later than Coronado's," Dr. Wedel told me. "However, there are many arguments on this score. Texas, Arkansas and Nebraska all claim that Coronado was there. I agree with others who think he traveled the Arkansas River into central Kansas, and it may well be that these pieces of chain mail were worn by his soldiers."

For clues to places to explore, the archaeologist often chooses a promising area and makes inquiry of local residents to see whether or not anyone has found Indian arrowheads or other relics. Frequently farmers find arrowheads while plowing. Sometimes an Indian mound stands undisturbed on a farmer's land.

"Many people believe that Indian mounds represent burial places," Dr. Wedel said. "Actually most mounds in Kansas were trash heaps two or three feet deep, though some were ten or twelve feet. Trash heaps are the best places for the archaeologist to dig, because that's where the residents threw broken pottery, broken tools, discarded housewares and other materials they could no longer use."

Old military posts and frontier forts offer good possibilities for archaeological finds. Recently at the site of Fort Sully near Pierre, South Dakota, archaeologists uncovered numerous bottles, knives, forks, gun parts and horse gear. Dr. Wedel's wife, who has had archaeological training, examined some old records of Fort Atkinson, founded about 1817, just north of Omaha, Nebraska. She came across a brief notation showing that two buck privates had been caught molesting an Indian grave. They were brought before their commanding officer, who let one off with a light sentence and discharged the other. "That soldier," Dr. Wedel said, "was probably the first man ever punished by the government for what we call pot hunting."

"Pot hunters" are amateur archaeologists who dig for souvenirs. Some of these enthusiasts have enough training to use reasonable care in unearthing specimens, and many have performed a real service to science. Others, however, have little or no real archaeological knowledge and may easily damage or even destroy artifacts that could be significant or scientifically important.

As in most of the other divisions, Dr. Wedel's branch has a research collection of countless specimens of archaeological discoveries. "Want to see something interesting?" he asked. "Look at this."

He stood up and removed the cover from a rough wooden box on a table. In the box I saw the flexed skeleton of a small child. Near the bones were thousands of disk beads made from river clamshells. Found intact at Medicine Creek Reservoir, about 40 miles from McCook, Nebraska, the skeleton was boxed and shipped to the Smithsonian, where it will be studied along with other materials from the Missouri River Basin.

The Missouri River Basin is an important archaeological area. Once heavily populated by American Indians, much of this territory has been and is being flooded by man-made dams. In a race against time and power shovels, men of the Smithsonian's River Basin Surveys are striving to salvage as much as they can of the materials that will throw more light on the lives, cultures and customs of the American Indian.

Chapter 5

Indians!

THOUSANDS OF AMERICAN INDIANS ONCE BUILT VILLAGES AND sat around council fires up and down the great Missouri River, which extends from Three Forks, Montana, to St. Louis, Missouri, and drains a basin of about 580,000 square miles.

Gradually the Indians were driven off their lands by the westward push of the white man, and hundreds of Indian settlements and military frontier posts were left at the mercy of the elements. The wind and the dust, the rains, the snows and the grass and weeds slowly but surely choked out the ruins, leaving only mounds or holes where huts, tepees and forts once stood.

Many village sites, some dating from the Ice Age, provided abundant specimens for studies of Indian life and culture, and so many of these locations existed that there was no great rush to explore them. Now there is, because in recent years plans were set in motion to build huge dams in various parts of the Missouri Basin. One of the first to be completed was the Fort Randall Dam in South Dakota, whose backed-up water flooded hundreds of the onetime Indian encampments, drowning countless archaeological and historical relics. Others now in progress will flood hundreds of sites, and the experts are racing feverishly against time and machinery to explore as many as possible. According to Dr. F. H. H. Roberts, Jr., Director of

49

the Smithsonian's Bureau of American Ethnology, an estimated sixty of these locations may be excavated before they go
under water. The others will be lost.

Since its earliest days the Smithsonian has conducted research into the history and culture of aborigines of North,
Central and South America, and its Bureau of American
Ethnology not only is concerned with Indians who lived in the
past but also studies living groups to get facts about their languages, institutions, social customs, beliefs, arts and crafts,
industries and physical characteristics. To understand them
properly it is necessary to know as much as possible about
their early history, which is why archaeological explorations
are so important.

When Columbus discovered the New World, about one
million Indians lived in America north of Mexico. Today
nearly half a million still live largely in the ways of their ancestors, who migrated from northeast Asia. Others have
adopted the external ways of the white man but have kept
their individual languages and tribal lore. Cultural remains of
ancient Indians exist in every state in the Union, but there is
no state where their history is adequately known and there
are several states where it is practically not known at all.

On one field trip Dr. Roberts made a series of diggings in
north Colorado, where he found several objects of the Paleo
Indians, an ancient group about which little is known. He unearthed several spear points, knives and stone hammers, along
with a few tools carved from bone. An analysis of charcoal
found with the implements showed that these Indians lived
about 9000 B.C. It appeared that the Paleos depended upon
hunting for food and clothing and that the main game animal
was a huge bison, a species now extinct and probably an an-
cestor of the buffalo. He also discovered that the Paleos had
killed and eaten native American camels (similar to the Peruvian llama), native American horses, giant sloths and a mammoth. The mammoth was as big as, or bigger than, our largest

elephant, yet these primitive people killed such beasts with crude spears.

Archaeological field trips are not without their hazards. On one expedition Dr. Roberts worked in a part of Arizona where large numbers of sidewinder rattlesnakes came out during the cool evenings. The camp was close to an old pueblo which the snakes used as a home.

"We wouldn't dare go outside at night without a flashlight for fear of stepping on a snake," Dr. Roberts said. "The trouble was, they weren't content to stay outside. One night when I was in bed I saw a big rattler slithering along a beam just above me. Before I could do anything he fell on me. I scrambled out, grabbed a shovel, scooped him outside and killed him."

On some mornings when he slept outdoors in a bedroll, Roberts found tracks in the sand where sidewinders had wriggled around him through the night.

After the Civil War, when there were clashes with the Indians, the government did not know how to classify the various groups, so the Smithsonian began a series of studies that resulted in classification of the tribes on the basis of language. With other field workers Major John Wesley Powell, first Director of the Bureau of American Ethnology, gathered vocabularies, sorted them out and produced a classification of tribes in the United States and Canada (later expanding into Mexico and Central America). Since virtually none of the tribes used alphabets or written records, the vocabularies were based on phonetics, the scientists writing words as they sounded.

Today field workers still go out and live with the Indians for two or three months to collect information and materials. Most of these experts know Arabic, Latin and Sanskrit, as well as modern languages, and they frequently use tape recorders to capture lengthy conversations in the Indian tongue for later study.

When the phonograph first came into use it recorded Indian

songs and conversations; but some of the older Indians refused
to say anything in the presence of the "machine that talks," on
the grounds that if it caught their voices they would be robbed
of something. Many also refused to be photographed for the
same reason.

"Even today in our Southwest there are villages where the
Indians have extensive ceremonies that people are forbidden
to photograph," Dr. Roberts told me. "The Zuñi in New Mexico hold rain dances and have Indian policemen circulating
through spectators to prevent picture taking. The Hopi will
take away visitors' cameras and check them until their ceremonies are over, and some will not even permit note taking
during the ceremonies." He grinned and added, "Some researchers have become quite adept at jotting down notes se-
cretly on small pads in their pockets, although they often have
trouble trying to decipher them later!"

There is one case in which Indian secrecy had an unusual
twist. Some years ago a group of Iroquois came to the Smithsonian to talk with a scientist named J. N. B. Hewitt, himself
of Indian ancestry, who had made a study of their culture.
Hewitt was known to have detailed information about an ancient secret Iroquois ceremony. The tribe had forgotten parts
of it and the "committee" spent two weeks with Hewitt to
learn the ritual of their ancestors, even including the words
and music of forgotten Iroquois songs which they took back
to their people!

All specimens collected by the Bureau of American Ethnology are turned over to the National Museum's Division of
Ethnology for display or study. The bureau, however, has a
tremendous collection of photographs of Indians, numbers of
which were donated by the Library of Congress after being
received from various exploring parties. Many were made in
the early 1860s and just after the Civil War.

I saw several photographs of Sitting Bull and an assortment
of pictures purporting to be Chief Crazy Horse, who led the

Oglala Sioux attack on General Custer at the battle of the Little Big Horn. There were several Indians known as Crazy Horse, and the Smithsonian has been unable to prove that any of its photographs are of the famous Oglala chief.

There are excellent pictures of Geronimo, the Chiricahua Apache chief who ravaged white settlements in the Southwest and who has been portrayed in countless wild West movies as both hero and villain.

I also saw a photograph of Two Guns White Calf, an Indian whose portrait many people mistakenly believe is on the buffalo nickel. James Earl Fraser, the sculptor who designed the Indian head on our five-cent coin, said that he made the face from a composite of three different Indians and that he never at any time saw old Two Guns.

One of the most impressive archives was a complete autobiography of Sitting Bull, who "wrote" the story of his life in pictures. Colored with crayon, they were drawn on the blank sides of many printed pages of the Roster of the 31st U.S. Infantry, U.S.A., which he or some of his braves may have captured or stolen from the army unit. Most of the drawings include a picture of a bull buffalo in sitting position, and a thin line extends from the buffalo to the mouth of one of the Indians shown in the picture (like a cartoon "balloon"), who is thus identified as "Sitting Bull."

Later the chief evidently learned how to write his name, for in the latter part of his picture story the drawing of the seated buffalo is replaced by the scrawled pencil signature, "Sitting Bull," near the Indian figure representing him.

The Smithsonian gets many requests from authors, historians and motion-picture companies for Indian photographs and other historical material, and Smithsonian scientists have themselves made numerous movies of Indians which are now stored in the National Archives.

One film company, just before World War II, made a movie called *Hiawatha*, for which a Smithsonian ethnologist served as a technical consultant. Censors refused to release the completed film on the grounds that it was too Communistic! Actually the Indians did live communal lives, and the Russians have used propaganda among their own people about the American Indian to show the advantages of communal living; but they fail to point out that the Indian ways were far from Communistic in the sense we know the word today.

An important source of research material is the Smithsonian's unique collection of paintings of Indian life by George Catlin, who painted more pictures of the real wild West than any other artist and whose work has been known for many years to anthropologists and ethnologists.

Born July 26, 1796, in Wilkes-Barre, Pennsylvania, Catlin as a boy thrilled to stories of Indian exploits. His own mother, as a young girl, had been captured by Indians in the bloody Wyoming Massacre of 1778. Catlin loved the outdoors and collected arrowheads and other Indian relics, but his father insisted that he study law. George passed the bar examination and set up shop in Lucerne, Pennsylvania, where he became so interested in art that he gave up his legal career and went to Philadelphia to devote full time to painting.

One day he saw a delegation of Indians from the far West who were traveling through Philadelphia on their way to Washington. Their rugged features and colorful costumes intrigued him and he later wrote, "The best study or school of the arts in the world . . . is the wilderness of North America. And the history and customs of such a people, preserved by pictorial illustrations, are themes worthy the lifetime of one man, and nothing short of the loss of my life shall prevent me from visiting their country and of becoming their historian."

Catlin's earliest known Indian work is an unfinished portrait of Red Jacket, the Seneca orator, dated at Buffalo, New York, in 1826. Later he accompanied General William Clark (of Lewis and Clark fame) while he discussed treaties with the Iowa, Missouri, Sioux, Omaha and other tribes. Catlin traveled up the Mississippi, the length of the Missouri, into Kansas, to Oklahoma Territory, down the Arkansas, making picture records of the Pawnee, Omaha, Missouri, Cree, Sioux, Arikara, Assiniboin, Crow, Blackfeet, Wichita and Comanche. At one time he traveled aboard the *Yellowstone*, first steamboat to ascend the Missouri, 2000 miles to Fort Union at the mouth of the Yellowstone River, and from the deck he painted landscapes of the lower river.

At first he painted or drew portraits of Indian chiefs, braves and squaws, but he later expanded his field to include Indian villages and scenes of Indian life and customs. Scenes included a Mandan foot race, the interior of a Mandan medicine lodge, an Osage brave lancing a buffalo, attacks on grizzly bears, buffalos fighting, war parties on the march, a Choctaw ball game, a canoe race, Indians spearing salmon by torchlight and an Indian family alarmed at the approach of a prairie fire.

Some of the names of his subjects are as fascinating as their pictures: Bloody Hand, chief of the Arikaras; Pigeon's Egg Head, Fire Bug That Creeps, Chief Buffalo Bull's Fat Back, She Who Bathes Her Knees, Torn Belly, No Fool, Hole in the Forehead, and Loose Pipe-stem, among others.

In all, he did between 600 and 700 paintings he called "Catlin's Indian Collection," and he exhibited about 500 of them for years in England and France.

Catlin became heavily in debt, and when preparations were made to auction off his belongings a wealthy Philadelphian named Joseph Harrison paid off his creditors and took most of his paintings as security. Two fires inflicted serious damage to some of the pictures, but when Catlin died in Jersey City, New Jersey, on December 23, 1872, the paintings were still in the possession of Mr. Harrison, who died a few years later.

In 1879 an Idaho lawyer, Thomas Donaldson, suggested that the Catlin paintings be salvaged and preserved. Joseph Harrison's widow agreed, and on May 15, 1879, she presented the paintings to the Smithsonian.

Many of them had been damaged by fire, water and insects; but today the Smithsonian has 445 of Catlin's remarkable pictures of the early West, several of which are on view in the Natural History Museum. The Division of Ethnology has entered into a contract with Henri Courtais of Boston to restore the Catlin paintings, a delicate task in which Mr. Courtais has shown that he excels.

Since Catlin's art predated the earliest photography, it is of immeasurable value to scholars and scientists studying the history, customs, homes, dress, weapons, tools and other aspects of the lives of the American Indian.

Indians of South America are also under study by Smithsonian scientists, sometimes with unusual objectives. In 1956 Dr. Marshall Newman, the anthropologist who told me so much about skulls and bones, organized a study of nutrition in a population of Vicos Indians in the Sierra Mountains of Peru, financed by the National Science Foundation and the Public Health Service (which was particularly interested in blood pressures, blood serum and cholesterol studies).

One reason he chose this group was that Cornell University did some research work there in 1951, had provided considerable information about the people and had established a friendly atmosphere.

He worked at a "broken-down hacienda" at 10,000 feet altitude, in an area covering about 45,000 acres. "I had to have an interpreter at all times, because the Indians speak *quechua* (ketch'-you-ah), the language of the Incas," he said.

Dr. Newman was told that the Indians raised cattle as "prestige" animals, used mostly for plowing with old-style Spanish wooden plows. Depending upon the number of cattle owned, a Vicos family was very poor, poor, medium, rich or very rich. The people raised a few chickens to get eggs, but the eggs were sold in the valley towns and were not eaten by the Vicos. Cows' milk was made into cottage cheese, also for sale. They raised corn and potatoes which were no larger than golf balls, sometimes as small as marbles. What little money the people earned went for salt, cloth and other simple necessities.

Dr. Newman was assisted by a Peruvian girl named Carmen, a trained dietitian. Before dawn each day he and Carmen visited each of six Indian families and weighed the food that they would eat for breakfast.

He measured the stature and weight of the people, working with a Harvard-trained Peruvian physician who made clinical studies of the children.

The children were getting only six to eight per cent of the Vitamin A they should have, and their diets were very short on calcium. With the money available to him (only $1200), Newman organized a program whereby 150 boys and girls in school would be fed six lunches a week for nine months in the year, each lunch providing 1000 calories. Powdered milk was furnished free by UNICEF, and the Nion Corporation of Los Angeles donated a supply of vitamin capsules. Although the Indians considered carrots unfit for humans to eat, Newman included carrots in school-lunch stews.

When the program was organized and his initial studies completed, Dr. Newman returned to the Smithsonian. Reports received from his helpers show that the children almost doubled their weight gain within two years. He is especially interested in their pattern of maturity. Will there be changes in the density of their bones? Will they grow into bigger men and women than their parents and grandparents were? Will the improved nutrition cut the rate of disease—especially of whooping cough, which is killing a number of youngsters not yet one year old?

In 1961 Dr. Newman hopes to return to the Peruvian mountains and see the results of his program. What he learns there he can apply to his studies of the human skeleton.

The American Indian displays on the first floor of the Natural History Museum are so arranged that the visitor may "travel" from the frozen North to the lower tip of South America. Life-size models of historic peoples, with specimens of their food, clothing, shelter, weapons and other objects are shown in sequence, from the Polar Eskimo to the people of Tierra del Fuego, southernmost inhabitants of the earth.

Many of the figures of people are so realistic that a woman once demanded that her Congressman take action to stop the Smithsonian from "shooting and stuffing all those Indians"!

One of the exhibits shows an actual Arapaho Indian tepee more than a hundred years old. If you think a wigwam was small, this one will surprise you. It is 17 feet high (about the height of a two-story house) and perhaps 14 feet in diameter, and is made with 16 stout wooden poles covered with 14 whole buffalo skins.

Buffalo skins, along with the skins of numerous other creatures, are of interest to another Smithsonian bureau, the Department of Zoology, whose experts study mammals, birds, insects, snakes, frogs, marine invertebrates and mollusks.

Chapter 6

Fins, Feathers and Hair

AN AFRICAN BIRD MAY GIVE DOCTORS THE KEY TO PREVENTING or curing tuberculosis, thanks to Dr. Herbert Friedmann of the Smithsonian staff.

Dr. Friedmann, Head Curator of the Department of Zoology, is also Acting Curator of its Division of Birds and one of the world's foremost ornithologists. On an African expedition in 1955 he made a close observation of the honey guide, a dull-colored bird about eight inches long with a sparrowlike bill.

The honey guide gets its name from the fact that it makes a loud cry as it flies from tree to tree in short hops, eventually reaching a tree or bush in which is a bees' nest with honey. The African natives often follow the "guide" to get the honey they know they will find at the bird's destination. Sometimes a honey-badger (a distant cousin of the skunk) is also led to the bees and digs the honey from the combs, his thick skin and fur protecting him against the stings of the angry insects. After badger or man has robbed the bee tree, the honey guide flies in to "mop up."

It was long believed that the bird ate the honey or the young bees. Dr. Friedmann, however, brought back evidence that, in addition to insects, they regularly and eagerly ate the wax of which the honeycombs were made. This was most unexpected, since wax was hitherto considered indigestible. Dr. Friedmann also found that a microbe in the stomach of the honey guide actually broke down the wax so that it could be digested.

He revealed his findings to medical researchers because, as he told me, "one reason doctors have so much trouble with a disease like tuberculosis is that the tubercle bacillus has a waxy coating that protects it against medication. The bacteria from the honey guide may help us to find a way to destroy the coating and to conquer tuberculosis." Resulting experiments have already prolonged the lives of guinea pigs suffering from tuberculosis.

On the basis of his work on the honey guides Dr. Friedmann was awarded the Daniel Giraud Elliott medal of the National Academy of Sciences in 1959 for meritorious work in zoology.

The bird displays at the Smithsonian are considered by some ornithologists to be the best in the world. Modernized exhibits "tell stories," such as the courtship and mating of birds, or their nesting habits, and the ways in which birds have been important to man.

One of the strangest of all birds was the object of an expedition sponsored by the National Geographic Society and the Smithsonian. The bird is the *hoatzin*, and little was known about it before this project began. Representing the Smithsonian was Mr. J. Lear Grimmer, Associate Director of the National Zoological Park.

The young hoatzin not yet able to fly can actually climb trees and swim! Ordinary nestlings, when danger threatens, huddle in the nest silently and helplessly; but the baby hoatzin, which lives along rivers and marshes, jumps from the nest into the water and submerges if it is in danger. At the "all clear" the baby goes ashore. It has sharp claws on its wings, with which it climbs the tree where its nest is. As the bird grows and develops feathers, the claws gradually regress and disappear. When grown, its wings are short and the bird flies in very clumsy fashion, sometimes crashing to the ground after a brief flight. Although the adult birds do not have claws on their wings, they do use the wings like arms in climbing trees.

Every bird in the Smithsonian's collection must be documented with facts as to the definite date and place of capture or discovery, the sex, whether young or adult and whether in breeding condition or not. From a mass of such material the scientists are able to piece together the life story of a species.

The museum is trying to work natural history problems into biological problems. Why do animals do what they do? Why does one bird have a shorter incubation period than others, or slightly different food habits? By understanding such differences the scientists get another approach to differences in various species.

The Department of Zoology, like most of the other Smithsonian bureaus, gets many letters from school children, obviously written at the suggestion of their teachers. Sometimes as many as forty letters are received at one time from one small town, each reading about as follows: "I have to write a composition about birds [or monkeys, or foxes, or snakes, etc.]. Please send me all the information you have."

Teachers who propose mass inquiries such as this may be doing an educational injustice to their pupils, who would learn more if they had to go to reference works to dig out for themselves the facts they need. The scientists agreed with me on this score and said that generally, in answering questions that ask for "everything" on a certain subject, they merely furnish a list of pertinent books that can be found in local public libraries. They all stressed the point, however, that they were more than happy to answer serious *specific* questions in their respective fields.

Dr. Friedmann pointed out one interesting fact about the Smithsonian animal displays. "In the art galleries the finest examples of original art are shown. In the natural history museum this does not apply. If you want to see a lion on display you can do better at the zoo than in Africa, where the lions wear off their manes on bushes and most of them look pretty mangy. The mangy lion may be useful to scholars or scientists who want to see him as he appears in his native habitat, but the better-looking lion would be the one on exhibit and might never have seen a jungle."

One magnificent mammal specimen dominates the entire rotunda of the first floor of the Natural History Museum. It is the Fénykövi elephant, largest land animal of the modern world, and it was unveiled at the Smithsonian on March 6, 1959. Standing 13 feet 2 inches tall at the shoulder, and in life weighing an estimated 12 tons, it is the largest elephant ever recorded. The famous Jumbo was at least 20 inches lower at the shoulder, and Jumbo was considered huge.

The elephant was donated to the Smithsonian by J. J. Fénykövi, a Hungarian-born engineer and big-game hunter now living in Madrid, Spain. The tracks of the enormous animal were first discovered by Fénykövi in 1954 while he was hunting rhinoceros in the uninhabited and largely unexplored Cuando River region of southwestern Angola, the big Portuguese colony in Africa. The next year he organized a special expedition from his hunting lodge at Humpata, and on November 13, 1955, finally tracked down the giant and shot it.

The elephant skin alone weighed more than two tons and required a whole truckload of salt to preserve it in the field. A crew of 23 natives could not lift the hide, but with more men and power equipment it was placed aboard a truck and carried through hundreds of miles of wilderness to the railhead at Silva Porto, 600 miles from the coast.

Smithsonian taxidermists William L. Brown and Norman N. Deaton were assigned to mount the skin. The beast appears to be moving at a fast walk, trunk lifted and ears fanned out. This in itself is novel; for most mounted elephants in museums are shown standing solidly on all four feet, lacking any impression of action.

I talked with Dr. D. H. Johnson, Curator of the Division of Mammals, who explained that the division studies various kinds of mammals to identify and name them, and to decide how they should be arranged in orders, families, genera and species.

"It is basic zoology," he said, "the primary identification of material. We want to know as much as we can about what kinds of mammals are in the world, how they are related to one another, where they occur and what names to call them by."

In Dr. Johnson's custody as Curator are 300,000 mammal specimens. A "specimen" generally consists of the skin and skull of an animal, although in some instances the whole body may be preserved. I saw a few thousand black bats in jars of alcohol. They had been captured by a Navy medical research team in Formosa and sent to the Smithsonian for identification.

Cabinets in the Division of Mammals are crowded with skins and skulls of all kinds and sizes, each numbered for catalog purposes. Some skulls are so tiny that Dr. Johnson uses a microscope to apply a pen-and-ink catalog number. Others, such as whale skulls, are so big that the number is applied with paint and brush. Whale skulls are not accompanied by whale skins because the skins are much too fragile. On a live whale a strip of skin could easily be scraped off the blubber with a fingernail.

As Dr. Johnson opened various cases to show me their contents, the air was filled with a pungent and rather unpleasant odor, caused by a mixture of ethylene dichloride and carbon tetrachloride used as a fumigant to protect the specimens. The skins of small specimens, such as mice, are not tanned but are treated with arsenic and stuffed with cotton, with wires in tails and legs to keep them straight. The arsenic also smells!

The skulls in the mammal collection are so white and clean that I asked Dr. Johnson what cleaning process was used.

"We clean 'em with live beetles," he said.

"Live beetles? What kind of beetles?"

"Dermestes beetles. Some people call them 'carpet beetles.' If you should find the carcass of a cow or other animal in a field, partly eaten by birds and bugs, and turned it over, you would probably find hundreds of carpet beetles under it."

"Just how do these bugs clean the skulls?"

"They feed on dried meat, hair, fur—anything like that. We put the skulls in with our colony of beetles and let them go to work. They leave the bone cleaner than a set of new false teeth! We've been using them since 1948."

Before they began to use this bug battalion, the scientists had to boil or steam the bones to get them clean; but about 20,000 of these hungry gray insects can strip all unwanted hair or skin from perhaps 2500 skulls (from mouse to hippopotamus) in one year. Although they do an excellent job, the museum keeps the beetles in a building away from its collections because the beetles would relish a feast on furniture, hair or fur, and could wreak havoc on many priceless treasures.

In Dr. Johnson's office I saw 14 caribou skulls mounted on the walls, along with one caribou head and one moose skull. He told me that the Smithsonian gets frequent inquiries from people who want to sell mounted mooseheads. "Many of these people are widows whose late husbands brought home mooseheads as hunting trophies. For years a wife hears her husband talk about his moose hunt with great pride and insist that his trophy should be in a museum. When the husband dies, the widow writes to us asking how much we'll pay for the trophy. She's usually surprised to discover that we have no use for it and that she might have to pay to have it hauled away!"

Other inquiries deal with identification of bones or teeth. One common type of letter says, "Enclosed is a tooth I found which is from a prehistoric monster. What animal is it from?"

The usual answer: "The specimen you sent to us is the tooth of a horse."

Sometimes the finders write back to argue with the scientists, who may have a hard time convincing them that a dinosaur's fang has no resemblance to a molar from the Old Gray Mare.

I asked Dr. Johnson if there was any particular specimen he wanted to add to his collection and he said he wanted to get the head of an Eastern Elk, a counterpart of the European red deer.

"Somehow the names of these animals got fouled up," he told me. "The original elk is what we now call a moose. When our forefathers came here from Europe they transferred the name of 'elk' to a deer, leaving the true elk without a name, and it came to be called a moose. Also the true buffalo is the old Indian water buffalo, and what we call a buffalo should be called a bison."

Another important branch of the Department of Zoology is the Division of Fishes, of which Dr. Leonard P. Schultz is the Curator. Unlike the Division of Mammals, Dr. Schultz's unit does not collect skulls and skins but has 170,000 glass jars of fishes "pickled" in alcohol, all jars neatly numbered and filed in evolutionary sequence, with the most primitive species at one end of the room. At first glance they look like rows of home preserves on pantry shelves.

This division acts as a sort of "Supreme Court" in the identification of fishes, especially those that need comparing with respect to types. Rules and regulations have been set up by the International Commission of Zoological Nomenclature governing the naming of animals and plants. Every specimen described is given a scientific name, and there is one specimen selected that represents the species. This specimen is called the *holotype*. Additional specimens used in the same description are known as *paratypes*.

The Division of Fishes has about 5000 holotypes and about 6000 paratypes, together with nearly two million other specimens, including many not yet processed and named. When a question comes up anywhere in the world about the identification of a fish that someone thinks might be the same as one of the Smithsonian's holotypes, Dr. Schultz and his associates compare the specimen with the holotype. If the species is not the same, they gave their expert judgment as to what it might be.

Before the atomic bomb tests at Bikini Atoll after World War II, Dr. Schultz and experts from the Fish and Wildlife Service went to the Marshall Islands to collect fish specimens. Using face masks, swim fins and dip nets, Dr. Schultz and three or four other men anchored their rubber boat over a coral reef to get various kinds of fish.

To collect the specimens, they poisoned the water with rotenone, a powder which, when used in the proportion of one part to 15 million parts of water, stupefied the fish so that they could be picked up with the nets. The rotenone, which affects the breathing apparatus of the fish, drove big eels out of holes into which they had burrowed tail first. The eels stuck their heads up a few inches and the divers grabbed them with canvas gloves.

In the course of six months they brought back about 35,000 fish to Washington for study. On another research trip in 1947 Dr. Schultz gathered additional specimens, one of which was a fish that spends its whole life in the belly of another creature, usually a large armless starfish about two-thirds the size of a football. The parasite, of the pearlfish family, is so transparent that its beating heart and circulating blood can be seen through its skin. Apparently it lives on food taken in by the starfish, and dies without emerging.

When I talked with Dr. Schultz he was making a world survey of shark attacks for the Office of Naval Research, aimed at finding ways to help people protect themselves against the man-eaters of the sea.

In 1959 there were 39 attacks by sharks throughout the world, 13 of which were fatal. There were ten shark victims in the United States, three of whom died. Five attacks took place off California, four off Florida and one off Georgia.

In August, 1960, a man bathing at Sea Girt, New Jersey, stood only knee-deep in the surf, unaware that a shark was streaming toward him in the shallow water. The shark struck, his wicked teeth tearing at one of the man's legs. The victim screamed. Lifeguards and others helped him ashore and found that his leg was almost bitten in two. An ambulance was summoned and he was rushed to the hospital.

After this incident several beaches were closed for brief periods and Coast Guardsmen and harbor police patrolled beach resort areas armed with rifles and machine guns to shoot any sharks that might appear near shore.

According to a report of the Shark Research Panel of the American Institute of Biological Sciences, it is well established that "sharks are frequently attracted to wounded or bleeding fish speared by skin divers. It is also generally agreed that the shark danger zone for a diver is at or near the surface, where movements are less likely to be rhythmic and coordinated. At least three of nine divers attacked while spear fishing or diving for shellfish in 1959 were attacked at the surface, and two of them were towing wounded fish at the time of attack."

January was the worst month for shark attacks south of the equator, and August in the northern latitudes.

Sharks, it seems, are unpredictable, and Dr. Schultz's project is aimed at accumulating more knowledge about shark behavior patterns and the conditions that may induce an attack.

Although the Division of Fishes has thousands of preserved specimens, and although skeletons of fish are on display in the Hall of Vertebrate Anatomy, few models of sea creatures were exhibited at the time of my research. One that attracts considerable attention is that of the coelecanth (seel'-a-kanth), popularly called a "living fossil." The first of these was landed in 1938 and created a sensation in the zoological world because this creature was believed to have become extinct some 70 million years ago, along with the dinosaurs, flying pterodactyls and other prehistoric reptiles.

Other marine specimens will be shown in a new Hall of Marine Life, now being modernized, and will include amphibians and reptiles. These are the specialties of a friendly lady, Dr. Doris M. Cochran, Curator of the Division of Reptiles and Amphibians. In her office–laboratory Dr. Cochran sits in the midst of jars of alcohol containing snakes, lizards, turtles, crocodiles, frogs, salamanders and their relatives. In all, she has about 150,000 specimens.

I saw pickled frogs half as big as footballs and just as brown. Originally bearing brilliant colors, specimens lose coloration in the alcohol and are all about the same chocolate shade.

"Did you catch those frogs yourself?" I asked.

"Yes, I did," Dr. Cochran said.

"I've never seen such whoppers. Where are they from?"

"Colombia."

"How'd you do it?"

"Well, mostly I collected at night, with a flashlight, because frogs are more active at night, especially during the breeding season. The light attracts them. I'd hold it in my left hand and wave it in front of the frog's eyes, then grab him with my right hand."

At the other extreme she showed me some specimens of Villavicencio frogs, also from Colombia, only about one inch long. "They jump sideways," she said, "and they're harder to catch than fleas!"

Flashlight-hunting was only one method of capturing specimens. Some frogs lived in air plants in trees, at the bases of leaves that held rain water. A man would cut down the plants and Dr. Cochran would take them apart to get the frogs.

Sometimes she would wade upstream with a dip net, or turn over big stones under which frogs might be hiding. I asked if any were poisonous.

"Oh, the toad has a gland behind the eye that secretes a whitish protein poison that's quite irritating to the mucous membrane of a wolf or dog or other animal that might pick up the toad," she said. "Also, in the Amazon the natives catch 'arrow-poison' frogs. They hold the frog close to fire or heat and a poison seeps from the frog's body. They scrape it off, let it ferment, then spread it on the tips of their hunting arrows. The poison on such an arrow will stop a bird or a small monkey, but probably wouldn't kill a big animal or a man."

Scientific knowledge of amphibians and reptiles is especially important in studies of tick-borne or mite-borne diseases. Studies of snakes helped man to produce antivenom against snakebite. Snakes, I learned, are of increasing importance in industry, especially in the making of shoes, bags or other objects once made only of leather.

"Snakeskin is much stronger than calfskin or pigskin," Dr. Cochran said. "It's becoming very desirable to catch the right kinds of snakes in sufficient numbers for industrial use."

A recent addition to Dr. Cochran's collection is a water-walking lizard from the Panama jungles. A relative of the chameleon, it has long toes fringed with scales that probably hold small pockets of air that provide buoyancy. If necessary the lizard can actually run across a small stream, although Dr. Cochran believes it might sink if it tried to dash across a big expanse of water.

Two other divisions of the Department of Zoology deal with water creatures. One is the Division of Mollusks; the other is the Division of Marine Invertebrates, of which Dr. Fenner A. Chace is Curator.

Marine invertebrates vary from tiny protozoans through sponges, jellyfishes, sea anemones, marine worms and earthworms, fresh-water worms, crabs, shrimps, lobsters, starfishes, sea urchins, sea cucumbers and sea squirts.

Every year members of Dr. Chace's staff make field trips to collect specimens, traveling to such places as the Nile River, the Caribbean Sea, the South Pacific and other likely areas. Their ultimate purpose is to determine what animals inhabit the oceans of the world.

They need many specimens because all animals, including man, vary in several respects, and until there is a substantial collection they do not know definitely what the species are. New species appear frequently. When Dr. Chace was at Harvard, a zoologist came to him one day and said he was getting strange reactions from earthworms in his laboratories and that his specimens did not react uniformly.

"What kind of specimens are you using?" Dr. Chace asked.

The man shrugged. "Just the common earthworm."

"Where did you get them?"

"In the woods back of the building."

The two men went to the woods, where Dr. Chace dug up and identified six different species of earthworms, none of which was the "common" type and two of which had never before been seen in Massachusetts!

When it comes to earthworms, America must take a back seat. In Ecuador and Colombia, earthworms reach a length of five to six feet; but even these are small compared to the Australian earthworm, which is sometimes eleven feet long!

When a new specimen (worm or other) is officially described in published form it is given a name. Many people think the best names are descriptive, but Dr. Chace points out that one can be "just as wrong with this system as with any other. For instance, you pick a specimen with a long spine and call it *Spinosis*, and a month later you find one with a spine twice as long."

Frequently the name of a locality is good, but then you may get a name attached to some specimen that did not come from that locality at all.

Some specimens are named for collectors or scientists who have worked on them. A man's name is Latinized by adding the letter "i" or "ii"; a woman's by adding "ae," or by adding "orum," or "arum," if more than one person is involved. This is followed by the name of the author of the official description and its date. There is one Japanese scientist named ii (pronounced ee-ee). One of the Smithsonian experts hopes he can someday name a specimen for him—it would be called iii or even iiii (pronounced ee-ee-ee-ee)!

All of these naming systems are in use.

A member of one South Pacific expedition was Dr. Harald A. Rehder, Curator of the Division of Mollusks, charged with studying the mollusks of the world.

These are found almost everywhere, from the depths of the oceans to the reefs, rocks and sands that fringe the continents; in tropical jungles and desert wastes; on high mountain peaks and in fresh-water streams, rivers and ponds. Mollusks include edible oysters, pearl oysters, scallops, clams, periwinkles, conches, cowries and whelks, as well as the most highly developed group of mollusks, the squid and the octopus. The garden slugs and common snails of our local woods and fields are mollusks, as are fresh-water mussels and "fingernail" clams.

Ordinarily we are not much concerned with mollusks, but they are closely connected with our lives. Oysters, clams and scallops are important food items. The shipworm, *teredo*, destroys pilings and other wooden structures on our coasts; during an outbreak of this pest in 1919–20 in San Francisco Bay the shipworm damage was estimated at about 21 million dollars.

Certain land snails are garden pests. Many fresh-water mollusks are directly implicated in severe diseases of man and livestock by acting as intermediate hosts to larval stages of parasitic worms, and it is estimated that about 100 million persons in China alone suffer from schistosomiasis (a frequently fatal disease involving the stomach, intestines and liver) induced by the Oriental blood fluke, a kind of worm.

How do the scientists get specimens? Dr. Rehder, who has been at the Smithsonian for nearly 30 years, told me about one of his trips. "We went out on the reefs in a dinghy and walked along the reefs, which were either out of the water or awash. Sometimes we swam along the inside edge of the reefs in the lagoons, using a face mask, or in shallow water we would simply pick up specimens whenever we saw them clinging to or crawling on coral rocks. We also did this along the shores of the mainland where there is coral or sand, and frequently we collected at night in shallow areas, because many snails that stay buried in the daytime will come out in darkness."

Occasionally they used a dredge in shallow water, in the form of a wire or mesh bag about 16 inches long. It was pulled with a rope behind a small boat with an outboard motor and simply scooped up whatever was in its path on the bottom.

Largest of all mollusks is the giant squid, sometimes measuring forty feet. Smallest is a species of land snail.

The biggest snail shell is the horse conch, from Florida. Largest clamshell is that of the giant clam—more than three feet long. "Is that the giant clam I've seen in the movies— the one that grabs a diver's foot and holds the diver under water?" I asked.

"That's it," Dr. Rehder said. "However, the movies exaggerate. Usually they show the giant clamshell snapping shut very swiftly on a diver's leg. Actually the giant clam closes his shell quite slowly. The shell has been known to catch a man's foot, all right, but any diver should be able to recognize and avoid it because the fleshy edge of the clam is brilliantly colored and looks like a big worm."

Dr. Rehder and other curators in zoology look forward eagerly to the completion of the modern Hall of Marine Life, where many of the strange creatures of sea and shore will be represented in new and fascinating displays.

One area of the Department of Zoology that presents display problems is the Division of Insects. Many insects are so tiny that they could not readily be seen, even under a magnifying glass, and models would be very costly to produce; so there are practically no insect exhibits, although there are millions of specimens in the study collections.

Most scientists believe that the first insects were wingless and that wings were the product of evolution. The first winged insects were called *Paleoptera*, and we know their only descendants as dragonflies and May flies.

We know about flies and ants and cockroaches and spiders, but there are thousands of unusual insects unknown to most of us. Take the acrocerids, for example. These are two-winged flies with very small heads. They pass the larval stage of their lives inside spiders and eat the tissues inside the spider shells, sometimes almost completely and without much awareness on the part of the doomed spiders. How the fly larva gets into the spider is anybody's guess. Possibly the egg is swallowed and hatched inside the body.

While the larva feeds on the spider, the spider continues its web weaving and other normal activities until very near the end. The spider dies and the little fly eats its way out of the stomach into the outside world, where it leads a normal adult fly existence.

If you ever see what you think is a bit of lace flying before your eyes, you're not seeing things. Chances are that it's a tingid, or "lace bug," distinguished from other flying insects by the delicate and intricate patterns of lacework that cover most of its back and forewings. Science has no answer as to the value of the lacy covering. "Perhaps it provides protective concealment," according to Dr. Carl J. Drake and Florence A. Ruhoff of the Smithsonian. "For similar reasons man himself makes use of nets or screens to camouflage strategic objects from the eyes of enemies, especially from the air."

The Division of Insects, headed by Dr. J. F. G. Clarke, studies the origin, distribution, classification and relationships of insects and related groups, including beetles; bees, wasps and ants; flies and mosquitoes; the true bugs, leafhoppers and cicadas; grasshoppers and crickets; butterflies and moths; white ants or termites; spiders, scorpions, centipedes and various minor orders.

Few of us realize that we are affected for good or bad by insects more than by any other group of animals. Food production demands a constant fight against plant-feeders. Man is subject to a dozen or more serious fevers transmitted by mosquitoes, fleas, lice and mites. Some of our food comes directly (honey) or indirectly (fruits, vegetables and other crops) from insects, and one of our most desirable textiles (silk) is an insect product. By and large, say the scientists, man probably has more to lose than to gain from the insects, and the fight against them must be constant. A knowledge of insect classification is essential to all other insect studies.

Many insects and other creatures are plant-feeders, but plants themselves are the concern of another Smithsonian bureau, the Department of Botany, where I talked with a young scientist who had actually walked and worked in The Lost World.

Chapter 7

The Plant Detectives

"THE LOST WORLD" IS THE TITLE OF AN ADVENTURE STORY written by the late Sir Arthur Conan Doyle, creator of Sherlock Holmes. It tells of a group of people who explored a South American wilderness in which man had never before set foot. There they found and battled with the dinosaur, the Stegosaurus, the Brontosaurus and sundry other prehistoric creatures that had mysteriously survived in this primitive land.

The book, of course, was fiction, but Doyle's description of the terrain and the climate and jungles was quite accurate. There is a part of Venezuela now known as The Lost World which was undoubtedly the scene of Doyle's adventure tale. I talked with Dr. Richard S. Cowan of the Smithsonian, who had set foot in this unusual place.

Dr. Cowan is Associate Curator of the Division of Phanerogams in the Department of Botany. I didn't know a phanerogam from a telegram until he explained that phanerogams are the flowering (seed) plants of the world, excluding the family of grasses. Among the major groups in the 300 families of phanerogams are cacti, peas and beans, potatoes, timber trees (pine, oak, walnut and mahogany), fruit trees, drug plants (such as those producing quinine and digitalis), latex-yielding plants (such as rubber) and horticultural plants (including orchids, begonias, roses, azaleas, lilacs and magnolias). Dr.

75

Cowan specializes in legumes—plants with seeds in pods, such as peas and beans.

When Dr. Cowan went to The Lost World he was a member of an expedition led by Dr. Bassett Maguire of the New York Botanical Garden. Once in South America, they hired Indians to carry their heavy equipment and set out for the mysterious region which, even today, is not geographically well known. Biologically it is known even less.

The party traveled by river whenever possible, using twenty-two-horsepower outboard motors attached to native dugout canoes. "The Indians loved it because they didn't have to pole or paddle," Dr. Cowan said.

As they plodded through the jungles the party met other Indians with whom "talks" were held in sign language. Occasionally an Indian could speak Spanish, but this was an exception.

Food was not a problem. The expedition carried canned corned beef, beans and rice; but these supplies did not last the scientists and the Indian porters for the entire trip, and when they were consumed the party lived off the land. Some of the Indians they met raised sweet potatoes and manioca (a tropical starchy plant), and provided bread and fish. In the forests they picked and ate berries and caught or shot game.

"The Indians would eat anything that moved," Dr. Cowan told me. "What they ate, we ate. The tapir (a piglike animal) is very good. It has red meat with a texture like pork and tastes like veal. We also ate giant guinea pigs and crocodile tails—all very tasty."

Monkeys were a regular part of the diet, but the scientists heartily disliked the Indian methods of monkey killing. A monkey that was only wounded by a shot or an arrow would be caught and promptly skinned by the Indians while it was still alive and screaming.

"There was one really unusual dish," Dr. Cowan recalled. "The Indians caught bird spiders—big, hairy things that looked like tarantulas. They get their name from the fact that they are supposed to be bird catchers. The Indians would simply toss a big spider, alive, on the coals of our campfire, let it sizzle a little while, then eat its legs just as we eat soft-shell crabs!"

After many days of trudging through the Venezuelan jungles the expedition reached The Lost World, a vast region of some 400 high sandstone mountains and plateaus standing as they have stood for thousands of years, virtually undisturbed by man.

There are at least one hundred mountains in the area that have never been climbed. "Many couldn't be climbed without regular climbing equipment," Dr. Cowan pointed out. "On a biological expedition such as ours you must find an easy way to go up, because you have to haul heavy equipment and supplies."

Even the "easy way" was difficult. To climb one escarpment, or steep cliff, the men had to use ropes and ladders made of saplings which the Indians tied together with vines. The cliff walls were almost vertical, but years of wind and rain had carved horizontal ledges, from a few inches to two or three feet wide, at various levels.

Slowly, carefully, the party climbed upward from ledge to ledge. "When I was about five hundred feet from the top the ledges ended," Dr. Cowan remembered. "We were about ready to go back down and try to go up on the other side, but then we found a 'chimney,' or hole, through the sandstone. We worked our way up through the chimney by clinging with our feet and fingernails until we found more ledges above us, then we continued to the top."

At the top the explorers gazed at the lush growth of plants and trees. "Knowing that we were the first humans to set foot in this primeval forest made it rather awesome," Dr. Cowan said. "We could see many of the other mountains, about thirty of which have been climbed, and I realized that the tops of these mountains are islands as truly as are oceanic islands, separated by altitude instead of water."

The mountains were considered by Indian inhabitants of the nearby jungles to be the dwelling places of their tribal gods, and many of the natives would not go there for fear of displeasing or disturbing these deities. There are many rivers and streams on the tops of the escarpments; and one spectacular feature of the area is Angel Falls, 3300 feet high and the highest waterfall in the world (about 20 times higher than Niagara).

Each mountain had its unique species of trees and plants, with the same species occurring on different mountains only rarely. The scientists found that the plants at the top were entirely different from those in the lowlands.

What grows in The Lost World? If you were to picture the tops of the mountains as one land mass, there are more plants that occur only there and nowhere else than there are on any island in the world. The men found numerous representatives of the madder family, which grows as a plant, a vine, a shrub and a tree; many members of the pineapple family, but none with edible fruits; several members of the camellia family with large flowers in brilliant colors; and a number of representatives of the chrysanthemum family which grow into large trees. About 95 per cent of the species collected grow on these mountaintops and nowhere else. About one-half of the specimens were entirely new species.

One surprising discovery would discourage any home owner with a power lawn mower. The scientists found giant grasses, some growing to a height of 25 *feet*! In one type the distance between joint areas in a grass stem was 22 feet, which means that the stem was mostly a long, straight hollow tube, ideal for the making of blowguns by the natives in the region. In fashioning the blowgun the soft center of a small palm tree is cleaned out and the grass stem is inserted, making it similar to the bore of a rifle. The palm trunk simply provides rigidity.

There were also giant pitcher plants, a different species of which is found along our own East Coast. Insects fall into the cup-shaped leaves of these carnivorous plants and are digested.

Rain fell every few minutes. They saw a few birds, some frogs and a species of opossum, but no other animals and no traces whatever of Conan Doyle's prehistoric monsters.

The collectors took specimens of all plants and trees that had flowers or fruits, as well as samples of various woods. Portable gasoline stoves were used to dry all specimens on the spot, after which the specimens were packed in bundles, with bug crystals to repel insects, and placed in boxes to be shipped home after the party reached the "outside." The boxes used for crating the specimens were carried in by the Indians and had been filled with newspapers (for packing specimens) and other disposable material used by the party. They also served as chairs at campsites.

In some other South American regions the men tried to find plants that were an index to deposits of bauxite, a claylike mineral from which aluminum is obtained, but their efforts were not conclusive. Some plants may betray the presence of minerals, as has been shown in the Colorado plateau country, where deposits of radioactive material such as uranium may be revealed by certain plants, including a weed known as "prince's plume" (*Stanleya pinnata*) and *Eriogonum*, the latter a tight cluster of small leaves on a stem so short it is barely visible. Protruding from the leaves are flower stalks about a foot high with very insignificant blooms. This is one of the Plains members of the buckwheat family. Another "index" plant is a species of locoweed (*Astragalus*) which accumulates selenium, a nonmetallic element that is associated with radioactive material.

After retracing their steps through the jungles and reaching the edges of civilization, the explorers presented a shotgun and a quantity of ammunition to the Indian chief as a special reward for his cooperation. The Indians would use the gun for hunting until the ammunition was gone—when they would return to their bow and arrow, awaiting the arrival of the next trader or until they went to a town where they could buy more shells.

The Smithsonian botanical collection probably includes specimens of 99 per cent of all the plants of the United States, according to Jason R. Swallen, Head Curator of the Department of Botany.

Mr. Swallen told me that the Smithsonian has about three million specimens of plants, grasses and woods, many of which he showed me. As in other bureaus, the specimens are neatly filed away in tiers of cupboards which are fumigated once each year. Special "poison doors" are installed on all cabinets for at least three days to insure that each one is fumigant-tight.

Although the department specializes in plants from North and South America and the Fiji Islands, its collections include specimens from all parts of the world, some dating back to 1750, many to the early 1800s.

An extensive index makes it possible to locate specimens quickly, and there are at least 80,000 index entries for grasses alone. The specimens are identified by their scientific names, and as we looked at a specimen of corn I asked Mr. Swallen to give me the botanical names for its various parts.

"The corn silk is the stigma," he said, "and there is a thread of corn silk for each kernel of corn in the ear. The pollen falls from the tassel, or staminate, to the stigma, producing the corn. The ear is the pistillate and the stalk is the culm."

As this was written, the Smithsonian had no public display of plants and grasses, but Mr. Swallen told me that one is contemplated for the future. Neither is there a Smithsonian display of the many kinds of woods, a subject I discussed with Dr. William L. Stern, Curator of the Division of Woods.

"Our work is devoted primarily to botanical research in woods," he said. "We have no special interest in the manufacture or conversion of wood into other products. We are largely interested in the microanatomy of wood and its association with the evolution of flowering plants. That is, using comparative wood anatomy, we find that the woods of certain plants resemble one another. Using this evidence, coupled with other data, we may assume certain relationships among plants. Just as the grass and external structure of plants indicate relationships and similarities among plants, so the internal anatomy is also useful in this regard. We can tell where certain groups of plants stand in the evolutionary scheme, just as zoologists can tell where animals stand."

To make such studies the Division of Woods now has about 20,000 wood specimens from such diverse kinds of woody plants as the bamboo, the sunflower, palms, and even some members of the lily family, including yucca. A laboratory for the preparation and study of microscope slides of wood samples is also an important part of the work on woods.

Wood specimens are accompanied by "herbarium vouchers," consisting of twigs bearing leaves and flowers or fruit from the specimen source. Without these it is sometimes difficult to identify accurately many species of plants from which the wood specimens come. The Smithsonian collection of leaves, flowers and fruits comprises the United States National Herbarium, which carries out studies in plant classification and nomenclature and also identifies and classifies specimens for collectors.

Among other things, I learned from Dr. Stern that most of the wood in every *living* tree is dead!

"Only the very outer part of the wood of the tree is alive," he explained. "The bark is not part of the wood, and the outer part of the bark, the part you see, is dead. Only the surface of the bark next to the tree wood is living. Sap, a combination of water and minerals, flows only through the living portion of the wood, though it soaks into other parts; and even where sap does flow, most of the cells are dead. The dead portions, of course, function as support for the tree and branches."

Trees and branches are sometimes the means of spreading the growth of plants to new territories. Plants and seeds sometimes take long trips by way of ocean currents, as shown by the "drift fruit" of South America.

The drift fruit is from the tropical tree *Sacoglottis amazonica*, a study of which was made by Dr. José Cuatrecasas, research associate of the Department of Botany. The tree bears fruit with a woody pit about as big as a walnut, but more oval-shaped. The pit has airtight cavities that enable it to float for years on rivers or oceans, and this is what it does.

Originating in the Amazon forests, the drift fruit is carried by the Amazon and Orinoco rivers to the Atlantic Ocean. The Gulf Stream then takes it to the West Indies and the coasts of Central America, where it has taken root and grown. Seeds have been found as far away as the shores of England and Scotland.

One unusual group of plants that ranges from your own back yard to the Arctic Circle and the equator comprises the ferns. Most of us have seen ferns from an inch to two or three feet high, but there are some which reach a height of sixty to eighty feet!

I talked briefly about ferns with Conrad V. Morton, Curator of the Division of Ferns, who has thousands of specimens in his research collections. Here are a few of the facts I learned from him.

The young unfolding fern we see in the spring and call "fiddleneck" (because it resembles the scroll at the end of a violin) is known scientifically as the *crozier*. Some species of fiddlenecks are edible and can be bought in stores, either canned or frozen. Others, however, are deadly and are among the worst poisoners of livestock. Warning: Don't try eating fiddlenecks you find in the woods!

Ferns grow as far north as the Arctic islands.

Thousands of people are fern collectors and belong to the American Fern Society.

Not all ferns are lacy in appearance. Some have solid leaves.

It is difficult to identify some ferns when they are fossils, because flowering plants may resemble ferns.

Ferns are among the oldest-known land plants and were probably the dominant form of vegetation 200 million years ago.

The root stock of one species, usually called the male fern, is of medicinal value in the treatment of tapeworm.

Ferns and many other plant specimens in the Smithsonian have come from an island wilderness in the middle of Gatun Lake, alongside the Panama Canal. Known as the Canal Zone Biological Area, Barro Colorado Island and its natural features have been left by law in their original state for study by scientists from the Americas. It is the only tropical scientific research station of its kind available in the New World to students and scientists, and it is part of the Smithsonian Institution.

Years ago, when a dam was built across the Chagres River to form Gatun Lake, a tropical forest on high ground became Barro Colorado Island. It is six miles square and, except for a few necessary buildings, is just as God made it—a reserve for tropical wildlife and plants. Naturalists, botanists, entomologists, ornithologists and other scientists visit the island often to do research in their particular fields.

With a rainfall averaging about 100 inches a year, the island's lush growth of trees and shrubs is covered with tropical vines so dense that fireflies show their lights in midday, and in a rainstorm a person can stand under the tree canopy for several minutes before drops begin to fall on him.

Wildlife includes monkeys, iguanas, sloths, anteaters, agoutis, jaguars, ocelots, tapirs, bats, snakes and numerous kinds of insects and birds, including the unusual antbird. This bird gets its name from the fact that ants provide its food, although it doesn't eat ants! Whole armies of ants frequently march through the jungles seeking food in the form of insects and their larvae. The ants are followed by small flocks of antbirds, and the ants flush out all manner of flying bugs and other insects on which the birds feast. Ornithologists who search for specimens of antbirds often follow columns of ants and soon find the feathered specimens they want.

A "nose count" of big red-mantled howler monkeys on the island was completed in 1960 by Dr. C. R. Carpenter, Professor of Psychology at Pennsylvania State University, and six associates. The howler monkey gets his name from his dawn chorus of roars, which sound like a combination of rumbling thunder and braying donkeys. Dr. Carpenter and his friends concluded that there are about 814 howlers on Barro Colorado. They build no nests, eat leaves and fruits and sleep in tall trees. They show their dislike for human intruders by pulling off dead tree limbs and throwing them at persons on the jungle floor, but their chief weapon seems to be the frightening, unearthly howl they make even as they travel.

Travel from the island to the mainland is by a 15-foot Fiberglas boat and a motor launch. A jeep has proved to be extremely useful for work in remote parts of the Canal Zone.

In a typical year some 50 or more scientists and students visit the island to live and make observations for several days, and others come to spend one day and a night. Visitors who come only for a day may number 400 to 500 in the course of a year. Some of the scientists have come from universities, museums or research organizations in most of the 50 states and from foreign countries, including England, Scotland, Belgium, France and Norway.

Barro Colorado Island is a world apart from another branch of Smithsonian activity that is quite different from any we have explored so far. This is where the visitor sees and scholars study old automobiles, early steam locomotives, power machinery, the first airplanes and other products of engineering and technology.

One unique attraction in the Arts and Industries Building is the Duryea automobile, a rebuilt carriage that was restored for exhibition thanks to the remarkable memory and help of a blind man.

Chapter 8

Eye for Invention

TWO BROTHERS, CHARLES AND J. FRANK DURYEA, OF CANTON, Illinois, built a gasoline-powered automobile which was tested successfully on April 19, 1892. It looked like a horseless buggy, with the engine under the seat; was steered by a rod, or tiller; and was called a "buggyaut."

Some historians claim that this was the first gasoline-powered automobile made in the United States. Others believe that there was an earlier car made by George B. Selden, who applied for a patent for an internal-combustion engine in 1879. The Smithsonian has Selden's patent model.

The first Duryea had a one-cylinder engine and iron tires on the buggy wheels. Later, at their shop in Springfield, Massachusetts, the brothers made a two-cylinder car with pneumatic tires and entered it in a round-trip automobile race between Chicago and Evanston, Illinois, on November 28, 1895. Here it was in competition with much heavier cars such as the Benz, the Daimler and others imported from Germany; but J. Frank Duryea drove the converted buggy across the finish line ahead of all the rest.

In 1920 a specimen of the 1893–94 one-cylinder "buggyaut" was presented to the Smithsonian. It was not in operating condition and needed considerable restoration work for exhibition purposes.

A few years ago the Smithsonian decided to replace missing parts and put the vehicle in good condition. Charles Duryea had died, but his brother Frank was still alive. He was a very old man, had been in retirement for several years and was completely blind. Would it be possible for him to remember enough about the engine to acquaint the Smithsonian's experts with its essentials?

E. A. Battison, who is now Associate Curator of the Division of Mechanical and Civil Engineering, and who has a private collection of antique automobiles, set out to get the information. Mr. Duryea was invited to the Smithsonian, where his sensitive fingers explored all the available engine parts and the places where some were lacking. As he recalled each part or feature he spoke into a tape-recorder microphone to describe it or to answer Mr. Battison's questions. With the recording, Don Berkebile, an ingenious, expert craftsman of the Smithsonian's Exhibits Staff, was able to restore the Duryea "buggyaut" and it is now on display in the Arts and Industries Building. It will later be exhibited in the Museum of History and Technology when the new building is opened, probably in 1963.

In the Hall of Transportation the visitor also finds early models of the Haynes, the Oldsmobile and the Simplex; Locomobile and White steam-powered cars; and the 1903 Winton, first automobile to be driven across the United States. There is an 1848 specimen of the Concord Coach, popularly known as the "Western stagecoach" although it originated in Concord, New Hampshire, in 1826.

A few steps from a crude, rugged Red River cart once used on the plains, is the "John Bull," the oldest complete steam locomotive in America, along with several models and relics illustrating the early development of our railroads.

The Division of Transportation is part of the Department of Science and Technology—which is headed by Dr. R. P. Multhauf, who selected the exhibits you will see in the Hall of

Power Machinery. Here are steam, gas and oil engines, water turbines and electric generators, so arranged that you may trace their development from early times to the present. Some have push buttons which you may use to see the machines in action.

Curator of the Division of Transportation is Colonel Howard I. Chapelle, a veteran naval architect who specializes in marine history.

"We want to show the complete history and development of land and water transportation in America," he said. "Right now we're collecting drawings or copies of drawings of transportation equipment so that we can make accurate scale models for our collection and exhibits."

Most models are built on contract by professional model makers or by gifted amateurs, including some members of the Washington Ship Model Society. At the time of my visit Chapelle's unit was working on models of ships of the Confederate Navy.

One unusual display will be a model of the first submarine designed and built as a freighter. Seven of these were built years ago in Germany, but only two were launched. One, the *Deutschland*, which visited Baltimore, Maryland, was converted into a fighting U-boat in World War II.

"With the development of atomic power," Colonel Chapelle predicted, "the time may come when we will use submarines as freight and passenger boats, so we want to show a model of the first submarine of this kind, even though it was not American."

Many of our modern devices aren't as new as we think. Some time ago a team of underwater explorers at Lake Nemi, about 40 miles from Rome, raised houseboats that had been built about 100 B.C. for use by the Emperor Nero. They were astonished to find roller bearings, ball bearings, double-action pumps, a complete plumbing system and very handsome cabinet work in these ancient wrecks. One vessel had been a floating palace, one a temple. The plumbing system used lead pipes fitted with valves. The portions of the boats under water had been covered with sheet lead to forestall damage by worms and insects.

I asked Colonel Chapelle to tell me the difference between a "boat" and a "ship." "Usually a boat is undecked and less than forty feet long," he said. "If it's decked and longer than forty feet, it's a ship." He grinned, and added, "You'll probably find some authorities with different definitions."

The Division of Transportation has plans or blueprints for about five thousand different vessels, including about a thousand drawings that were Colonel Chapelle's private property when he came to the Smithsonian. The most ancient plan of an American vessel is the British Admiralty drawing of the sloop *Mediator*, built on Chesapeake Bay in 1741. The oldest plan of any kind in the collection is that of a British ship of 1697.

The division gets about five serious inquiries a week and a number of foolish ones. One request was for a photograph of the first steamboat "built by Fulton Lewis, Jr." (a radio commentator). One letter asked for a photograph of "the first boat ever built by man."

When the Smithsonian turned down an offer of a novelty ship model made of match sticks, its maker objected. "This model won a prize in a local contest," he said. "The Smithsonian accepted the Hope Diamond. Why won't it accept my model?"

The Transportation Division has numerous specimens not on public display. Eight old automobiles and five ancient carriages are in storage. There are scores of small patent models of automobiles, locomotives, fire engines and carriages, a few of which are on view in the hall. The reference collection includes hundreds of accessories—carburetors, headlights, locomotive whistles and bells, sections of steel rails, spikes and other construction materials.

In storage awaiting completion of the new Museum of History and Technology is a 150-ton steam locomotive, 90 feet long, a gift of the Southern Railroad. Known as P.S. 4, Pacific Type, No. 1401, this engine was built in the Richmond, Virginia, Works of the American Locomotive Company. When this and the small models and other railroad objects are assembled in the new building, they will represent the only place in the United States where one may see the complete development of the steam locomotive.

John R. White, Associate Curator of the Transportation Division, told me that maintenance of the exhibits on display presents a problem.

"Visitors always want to touch the vehicles," he explained. "We get perhaps six million visitors a year, and a few million finger tips wear down the paint on our old cars to the bare metal. The paint has to be renewed, and within two years it's worn off again. Unfortunately some of the youngsters in school groups are vandals and have broken off headlights and other accessories. Some have even stolen oil cups from the engines, but our guard force makes it pretty difficult for anyone to take such things out of the building."

Mr. White considers the most unusual transportation specimen to be the relics of the "Stourbridge Lion," the first steam locomotive to operate on the North American continent. It was bought by the Delaware and Hudson Canal Company, which operated a short railroad in connection with a mine; but the locomotive was too heavy for use on wooden rails, so it was put into storage. A few years later the company tried unsuccessfully to sell it. Gradually the owners began to remove parts to be used on other machinery, and in the 1840s they sold the boiler and one cylinder to a factory which set it up and ran it as a stationary engine.

In the 1880s the boiler was so badly worn it was thrown on a junk heap where it was discovered by J. E. Watkins of the

Smithsonian, who obtained it for the museum. Eventually he located the few other parts that have been preserved.

The Smithsonian would like to fill several gaps in its transportation collection. One welcome accession would be an early American-type locomotive, 4–4–0 (four small leading wheels, four driving wheels). Others: a gasoline-electric automobile; a "motor wheel," which is a little bicycle wheel, with a gasoline motor attached, that can be bolted to an ordinary bicycle; a cycle car, a four-wheeled affair that looks as though it were built of bicycle parts; and finally, any mechanical drawings or blueprints of locomotives, streetcars, trucks, busses, automobiles, fire engines, carriages or wagons.

The Smithsonian would also like to add to its collection of early hand and machine tools, according to E. S. Ferguson, Curator of the Division of Mechanical and Civil Engineering. When I talked with Mr. Ferguson he was helping to prepare an exhibit for a Hall of Tools in the new Museum of History and Technology—an exhibit that will try to show the development of machine tools with hand-tool ancestors. It will include a completely equipped pre-Civil War machine and chronometer shop, 23 by 28 feet, built of materials used originally in an old wooden clock factory in Connecticut. Most of the machine tools were made before 1855 and several came from a small Rhode Island machine shop built in 1850.

"Practically no satisfactory history of machine tools exists," Mr. Ferguson said. "For straight wood-turning we can go back to the potter's wheel, the first machine to generate a geometric figure, which is the same thing our lathe does today. In drilling we can go back to the Egyptian bow drill, pictured in tomb paintings."

Mr. Ferguson believes that the history of engineering and technology has been neglected in our educational system. He developed interest in this kind of history while he was teaching mechanical engineering at Iowa State College; but when he found that students and engineers had little or no enthusiasm for history he joined the staff of the Smithsonian, where he and others can do research and show the progress and development of the engineering sciences.

One man recently wrote to Mr. Ferguson saying that he understood the Smithsonian had a standing offer of $5000 to be paid to the inventor of a successful perpetual-motion machine, and that he had an idea for such a device. The Smithsonian has no such standing offer. Another man sent in a sketch of a proposed perpetual-motion machine, saying, "The Smithsonian can build it. All I want is the honor of having introduced it."

"Introducing" inventions of any kind may involve all sorts of tangles, and sometimes the identity of the inventor who perfects a device is obscured by the greater fame of another who uses it. During my research I learned from one Smithsonian expert that the first commercially successful phonograph was invented not by Thomas A. Edison, as most people think, but by Charles S. Tainter, working with Alexander Graham Bell. Edison made the first audible recording of sound; but Tainter and Bell made improvements in the instrument, and the Edison phonographs offered for sale were produced under license from the Tainter patents. Examples of the machines are in the public exhibits.

Edison's accomplishments are well represented in the Smithsonian's Division of Electricity, where Curator W. J. King, Jr., maintains a collection that includes one of the earliest Edison generators, a replica of the first carbon filament lamp and the Edison dynamo used on the S.S. *Columbia* in 1879.

Displays include the early telephones of Edison, Bell and other inventors, the first Morse telegraph instruments, and relics and models showing the progress of these methods of communication.

Some specimens in the reference collection are too large to be displayed or even stored by the Smithsonian. The first Navy radar, for example, has an antenna so huge that it would not fit into the building. The Smithsonian has the electronic gear used in this device, but will have a small model of the antenna made for display purposes.

In the new Museum of History and Technology the Hall of Electricity will present an educational history of electrical technology from the days of early experiments to the present. A recent acquisition for the display is the world's first betatron, an atom-smashing electron accelerator developed by Professor Donald W. Kerst at the University of Illinois in 1940. It is not much bigger than a man's large-size suitcase and produces two and one-half million volts of electricity. In contrast, Professor Kerst in 1950 built a 340-million-volt betatron, largest in the world, at the university.

One of the most famous electrical experiments on view is represented by a model showing the moment when Benjamin Franklin flew a kite in a thunderstorm to prove that lightning and man-made electricity were one and the same. Incidentally, in 1753 a Russian scientist, Professor Georg Richmann of St. Petersburg, was the first man to be killed in trying to repeat the Franklin experiment using ungrounded electrical apparatus.

One of the more fascinating places in the new Museum of History and Technology will be the Hall of Timekeeping, under the supervision of Associate Curator Edwin A. Battison of the Division of Mechanical and Civil Engineering.

Many timekeeping devices now on display in the Arts and Industries Building will be moved to the new museum and shown in an expanded exhibit. Along with early watches and clocks are examples of the sundial and the water clock, or clepsydra; the candle clock and the slow-burning rope. A huge tower clock still keeps good time, although its movement has been in use since 1797.

"America led the world in the manufacture of clocks in the nineteenth century," Mr. Battison told me. "They started with wooden clocks, then went to brass. You may be surprised to know that automation existed in the Waltham Watch Company factory in the eighteen-eighties."

He showed me an example of this automation in the form of a small machine where a piece of material was placed in a hopper at one end, picked up by a movable arm and carried to another position, picked up by another arm and moved again, through several steps. At each step some mechanical operation was performed; and when the piece of work was lifted by the last arm it was dropped in a box at the other end of the machine, finished.

Another surprise: Automatic-winding watches were developed in the late eighteenth century!

The Smithsonian has the first chronometer made in the United States and all of the equipment used in the workshop of its maker, William Bond of Boston. Bond's son devised the first chronograph, and the Smithsonian has what may be the first chronograph made in that shop.

I asked Mr. Battison to explain the difference between a chronometer and a chronograph.

"The chronometer is a very precise time-measuring instrument," he said. "Its escapement [a device that controls the motion of gears or pendulum] is less subject to changes because of oil, temperature, humidity or other factors that might affect an ordinary timepiece. It is actually a highly refined clock or watch, and one necessity for the high refinement is the observation of heavenly bodies in navigation. If a clock or watch were not precise when used to navigate by the stars, a ship might veer off course and hit a reef or shoal."

"And the chronograph?"

"The chronograph shows distances between places by timing the passage of heavenly bodies. It makes a recording of the passage of time." An ordinary stop watch might be considered a crude form of chronograph, but true chronographs are precision devices with paper tape or other material on which pens make marks representing the minutes and seconds.

Timepieces are classified by the Smithsonian as "light machinery," a designation which includes typewriters, phonographs, music boxes and other small mechanical devices. Displays tell the whole story of the typewriter through a replica of the first typewriter and original Patent Office models. Old and new models of calculating and other office machines are also on view.

Perhaps the greatest machine of all time is the human body, and its workings are well explained in the Smithsonian's Hall of Health as part of the Division of Medical Sciences in the Department of Science and Technology. Curator of the Division is Dr. John B. Blake. Associate Curator is Dr. Sami Harmaneh, with whom I talked.

Dr. Harmaneh, a naturalized American citizen who was born about fifty miles east of Jerusalem, specializes in pharmaceutical research and has a Ph.D. degree from the University of Wisconsin.

The Division of Medical Sciences was called the "Section of Materia Medica" when it was established in 1891. The term *materia medica*, meaning drugs or other substances used in medicine, originated as the title of a monumental work written in the first century of our era by Diorscorides, a Greek physician who accompanied the Roman army on its conquests. In his book he described various plants and told what they were good for, how they could be collected during the seasons and how they should be used in treating disease.

The division's reference collections, which fill cabinets and cubbyholes in all available storage space, include specimens of crude drugs from plant, animal and mineral sources in every corner of the world. Many of these are also in cases on display, although the exhibits do not include any habit-forming drugs because of the danger of theft and because such displays might induce curious or impressionable people to experiment with harmful substances. The collections in storage, however, include opium and other habit-forming drugs, and even opium pipes. In all, the division has around 15,000 specimens for research purposes, among them tools and other equipment used by pharmacists and pharmaceutical manufacturers.

Years ago various parts of plants (roots, leaves, flowers, gums) were in wide use as medicines, and many a family doctored itself by brewing spearmint or sassafras tea, eating rhubarb as a laxative, or smothering a boil under a flaxseed poultice to "draw out" the infection. Quinine, still used extensively in fighting fevers, is a product of the cinchona tree.

In recent years the medical world has discovered that many of nature's products have amazing combative effects on disease, and medicinal plants long forgotten are now being used in modern experiments in the battle for health. The Smithsonian's extensive collection of specimens may help to win that battle.

The collections include a wide variety of instruments used in dentistry, and one exhibit that seems to amuse many visitors is the equipment used by the late Dr. G. V. Black, an Illinois dentist who invented the cord-driven foot-powered dental engine. His dentist's chair is upholstered in gloomy black leather, with a matching headrest, not designed to cheer patients. All of Dr. Black's dental instruments, however, had pearl handles.

Dr. Harmaneh is quite proud of the fact that his exhibits include the hypodermic syringe used by Dr. Jonas Salk in developing the wonderful Salk vaccine to prevent polio. Dr. Harmaneh showed me a reproduction of an Egyptian *stele* (stone slab) with carved figures of a man and woman. The man carried a staff and has a badly deformed foot and leg, indicating that polio was a scourge even in ancient Egypt.

The display most highly prized by the division is a reconstructed Old World apothecary shop, complete to the rough floorboards, drug jars, fifteenth-to-nineteenth-century fixtures,

Towers and battlements of the
Smithsonian Building. Designed after
a 12th century Norman Castle.
Flag tower is 140 feet high.

Smithsonian Museum of
Natural History, south side

New Museum of History and Technology. Drawn by Hugh Ferriss

Freer Gallery of Art

Art and Industries
Building

Barro Colorado
Island, Gatun Lake,
Canal Zone.
Biological Area
administered by the
Smithsonian
Institution

James Smithson, founder of the
Smithsonian Institution
(From a miniature by Johns)

Joseph Henry, first Secretary of the
Smithsonian Institution

Dr. Leonard Carmichael, present
Secretary of the Smithsonian Institution

TenyKövi elephant, the largest land animal ever prepared for exhibition

Skeleton of an armored dinosaur. Behind the Cub Scouts is a lifelike reconstruction of the beast.

Dr. Robert Goddard who opened
the way to space exploration,
with a pioneer rocket

The Kitty Hawk Flyer, the
first heavier-than-air
flying machine

Lindbergh's Spirit of St. Louis

Hall of Transportation with John Bull locomotive in foreground

All that remains of
the original
Star-Spangled Banner

The one-cylinder
Duryea, first of the
"horseless carriages"

The Hope Diamond,
44½-carats

Largest perfect crystal
ball in the world,
106 pounds

Ancient Egyptians mummified animals as well as humans

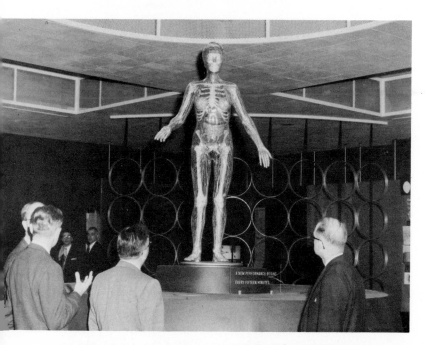

Brunhilde, the transparent woman in the Smithsonian's Hall of Health

Diorama showing how Indians sometimes killed buffalo by driving them over cliffs

Many exhibits such as this show lives and customs of Eskimos and Indians of the Americas

Old world apothecary shop—Europe, 15th-19th century

A doll house with specimens of furnishings found in American homes early in the 20th century

A room in First Ladies' Hall showing the dresses of (l to r) Dolley Madison, Martha Jefferson Randolph, Martha Washington, Abigail Adams

Secretary Carmichael shows First Ladies' gowns to Mrs. Eisenhower and Queen Elizabeth of England, November, 1954

Sculptor A. J. Andrews with head of native of Arnhem Land, modeled from
face mask and photographs

Baker-Nunn satellite-tracking camera used to photograph satellites in orbit

Artist puts finishing touches on display background to blend with mounted specimens of real lemmings at center, right

Fading of colors on some mounted specimens requires occasional retouching

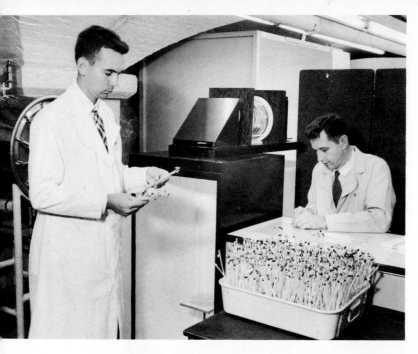

Studying string-bean plants grown in darkness to determine effect of light on growth

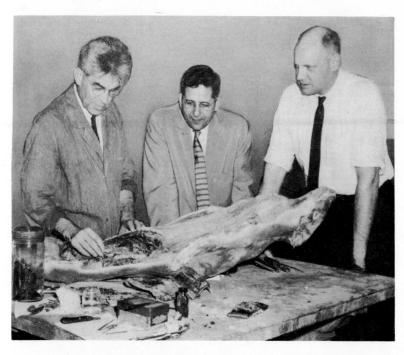

Removing tissue samples from mummified crabeater seal brought from Antarctica

Divers Link and Peterson examining an 18th century wreck in 35 feet of water. In the background is an electronic metal detector.

Excavating at a deeply buried occupation site in the Angostura Reservoir Basin, South Dakota

utensils, books and documents collected from European countries over a period of many years by Dr. Jo Mayer of Wiesbaden, Germany. Mounted on the walls are stuffed turtles, alligators and other animals which were calculated to convince customers that when they bought their turtle oil or other concoctions they were getting "the real thing." Books in the shop were printed in the 1700s. One bronze mortar has a date cast in relief: 1699.

The one object that fascinated me most in the shop was a chest which some ancient druggist had used as a safe. It is about the size of a small trunk, but is massive in appearance and has a huge keyhole on the front side. A giant iron key lay on the top of the chest, but I discovered that when I put the key in the keyhole it would not turn and the chest remained locked. My guide laughed and manipulated a panel on top of the chest, sliding it aside to expose another keyhole which was the *real* one! The other was simply a decoy to fool robbers.

Visitors to the Hall of Health learn many things in a few minutes about the function of the human body. Principal attraction in the hall is Brunhilde, "the transparent woman," a life-size female figure, made in Germany, whose clear plastic body reveals nerve structure, veins and arteries. Brunhilde stands on an elevated revolving platform and, as she turns, a recorded voice explains the purposes of the heart, the liver, the stomach and other internal organs, each of which lights up as it is being described.

At one end of the hall begins a story called "The Birth of a Baby." Relief plaques mounted on the wall show how a baby grows in the womb and how it comes into the world, and explains what takes place at each step. One case contains actual embryos from three weeks to seven months old, so that the progress of growth can be clearly seen.

A display about the heart shows that this amazing organ beats about three billion times in seventy years, pumps a total of 250 million quarts of blood (enough to fill a football stadium) and does an amount of work equal to that required in lifting the biggest battleship fourteen feet out of water.

There are displays involving most parts of the body—the glands, the nervous system; the eye, ear and brain (there is an actual human brain encased in plastic); and in one corner of the hall there is even a tiny theater where colored slides are shown every few minutes to explain some interesting phase of bodily functions. The slide program is changed monthly.

Health education such as this has been a great benefit to mankind. In the Bronze Age in Greece the average person could expect to live about eighteen years. Today the life expectancy of the average person in the United States is seventy years or more.

The work of some of the divisions of the Department of Science and Technology may overlap that of another Smithsonian bureau, the Department of Arts and Manufactures, created in 1957.

Dr. Philip W. Bishop, Head Curator, also directs the Division of Industrial Cooperation.

"On the grounds that history is made from day to day, I keep in touch with private industry in five fields," he explained. "These are Petroleum, Nuclear Energy, Mining and Mineral Processing, Iron and Steel and General Manufacturing. In many of these we can work out modern cooperative educational exhibits with the manufacturers."

Recently Dr. Bishop located and obtained the original Burton Humphreys still, which was used to produce gasoline in the quantities that the early mass-produced Ford cars demanded. When Model T Fords began to roll off the assembly line, the principal product of the oil industry was kerosene. The plants had to find a way to produce gasoline in big quantities. Humphreys designed a pilot still which became the first break-through in the production of gasoline.

The development of the oil industry will be shown in new exhibits in the Museum of History and Technology, from a model of the first oil well to the latest methods of making high-octane fuel for aircraft.

At the time of my visit Dr. Bishop was working on plans for a nuclear-energy display. "We want to explain, clearly and simply, how the concept of atomic structure grew and how scientists went from step to step until they reached the point of fission," he said. "We won't deal with the atom or hydrogen bomb—only with the peaceful uses of atomic energy."

Other attractions will deal with coal mining from its earliest history to the present and will show how iron ore is converted into iron and steel and then into products such as wires, tubes and sheets.

Both "arts and manufactures" are represented in the Division of Graphic Arts, whose displays include the actual printing press on which Benjamin Franklin once worked in London.

F. O. Griffith III, Assistant Curator, showed me a few of the 50,000 specimens of etchings, engravings and lithographs in the study collection, some by famous artists such as Dürer, Rembrandt, Daumier, Goya and Picasso.

In the Hall of Graphic Arts, where we looked at several early printing presses, I noticed a huge statue showing George Washington seated as though on a throne, virtually naked to the waist and draped in a toga. The work of the American sculptor, Horatio Greenough, this statue was the first ever commissioned by Congress. It was unveiled in 1843 and drew considerable criticism from citizens who protested that Washington was made to look too much like some Roman general or even an emperor. Some called it "the naked Washington." It is in a part of the Smithsonian Building called "The Chapel," which looks as though it were originally designed as a church.

The research collections include print-making tools, printing presses, bookbinding and papermaking devices, the first Mergenthaler linotype machine and a page from the Gutenberg Bible.

The Graphic Arts Division also has an excellent accumulation of all sorts of photographic devices dating from the earliest cameras and lenses, providing a complete history of the technical development of the art of photography. There are numerous examples of black-and-white and color photos of all periods, including some of the famous Mathew Brady pictures.

Another "arts" section of Arts and Manufactures is the Division of Ceramics and Glass, where I learned from Curator Paul V. Gardner that although most people have heard of "chinaware" no one can define it exactly.

"You can ask a hundred authorities for definitions and get a hundred different answers," Mr. Gardner said. "The British called 'china' any pieces that were actually brought from China. There isn't any 'china' unless it was made in China. Calling dishes 'chinaware' is as wrong as describing a building as a 'New England house.' "

Mr. Gardner is working on plans for a ceramics and glass exhibit in the new museum building. "We'll start with an introductory gallery showing materials and methods of manufacture," he explained, "then a geographical summary of ceramic developments as far as our collections permit, beginning with a German room showing fourteenth-century ceramics from Germany, the first country that knew how to make true porcelain."

In ceramics, as in many other fields, many attempts have been made to fake marks and ages. Much French porcelain carries counterfeit marks to trap tourists into paying high prices for what they wrongly believe are treasures.

"Some fakes are beautifully done," Gardner said. "One set was brought in here by a woman from New Orleans who said it had been authenticated by a reputable dealer there. I told

her that some dealers are genuinely fooled by expert counter-
feiters and that some also sell fakes knowingly."

One type of pink porcelain, called "Rose Pompadour," is
among the kinds most frequently imitated.

Sometimes even experts cannot be sure where or by whom
a particular piece was made, because many early craftsmen
went from factory to factory taking their skills and distinctive
workmanship with them.

Some specimens are good for laughs. For example, German
artists who had never been near China painted vases and other
"china" with Chinese figures wearing British or German hats,
or they added European architectural touches to Oriental
structures.

Visitors often bring ceramic or glass objects to Gardner's
office for identification. One day a man brought in a panel of
Millefiori glass, a distinctive kind of glass mosaic. He had
taken it to several dealers who told him that it was made during the eighteenth or nineteenth century. One, however, suggested that it had been made by Steuben, where beautiful
ornamental glass is still produced. The owner thought that this
suggestion was ridiculous and he decided to bring the piece
to the Smithsonian to get a definite opinion, if possible.

Gardner examined it carefully. "I can identify this piece
positively," he declared. "It did come from Steuben."

The visitor looked skeptical. "How do you know that?"

Gardner smiled. "Because I made it myself," he replied.

When he was about twenty years old Gardner had worked
in the Steuben plant and while there he had made this copy
of the Millefiori panel.

Gardner's research collection ranges from paperweights
(about 400) to one of the finest specimens of eighteenth-cen-
tury cameo glass, the result of six years of carving by one
English craftsman. The oldest piece in the collection is an
Egyptian flask made about 1500 B.C., probably used by some
Egyptian flapper for cosmetics.

Leaving Mr. Gardner, I visited Grace L. Rogers, Curator of the Division of Textiles in the Department of Arts and Manufactures. She is concerned not only with fabrics themselves but also with fibers used to produce them and the machinery that transforms the fibers into yarn and cloth. Her collection includes primitive spindles and looms and many nineteenth-century American patent models, all designed to show the development of cloth making from the spinning wheel through the important inventions of machine spinning.

The questions she and her staff are asked provide a good idea of the range of her research material. Some bring in old sewing machines for identification. She has an outstanding collection of sewing machines, including the 1851 patent model for the Singer and more than a thousand other patent models.

"Basically the sewing machine has not been changed, except for being streamlined," Miss Rogers told me. "Even the so-called zigzag stitch was invented in the nineteenth century."

Women bring in quilts and coverlets, pieces of toile, brocade found in old trunks or in antique shops, yarn winders, parts for spinning wheels and other items. In most cases they get answers to their questions, because Miss Rogers has examples of fabrics for every decade through the past hundred years or more; a big collection of quilts, samplers and other needlework; hundreds of natural fibers (jute, hemp, cotton, flax, etc.) from all parts of the world; scores of pincushions and thimbles; and many spinning wheels and looms used in Colonial America. There is an impressive collection of sixteenth-to-eighteenth-century lace, mostly hand-made and of European origin, and a good sampling of nineteenth-century machine-made lace. Hand-made and machine-made rugs are also available for research.

Miss Rogers told me that her collections, although extensive, are lacking in examples of seventeenth-century textiles and that she would be pleased to hear from anyone who would donate such specimens to the Smithsonian, where they will be properly preserved.

Preservation of textiles and machinery presents certain problems. Textiles are stored in drawers along with naphthalene and moth crystals to keep out moths and insects. Cloth that is especially fragile may be mounted on linen or some other substance—making it easier to handle. Care is taken to prevent rust and deterioration of the textile machinery.

Miss Rogers has been at the Smithsonian since about 1946, when she graduated from the University of Maryland, where she majored in studies of fibers and weaves. Soon after she started her work she was walking through the museum one day when a woman visitor said to her, "Excuse me, but can you tell me where I'll find the *Spirit of St. Louis?*"

"Just go to the North Hall, and you'll see it suspended from the ceiling," Miss Rogers replied.

The woman started to walk away, then stopped and came back. "By the way," she said, "just what *is* the *Spirit of St. Louis?*"

It seems that friends in her home town, knowing that she was to visit the Smithsonian, had told her, "Be sure to see the *Spirit of St. Louis,*" but she had no idea what it was!

The *Spirit of St. Louis* hangs in the Arts and Industries Building, where its famous pilot, Colonel Charles A. Lindbergh, once wanted to climb a rope to get back into the plane's cockpit.

Chapter 9

Wings Brave and Bold

ONE DAY, LONG AFTER THE SMITHSONIAN HAD ACQUIRED THE *Spirit of St. Louis,* a telephone call came to Mr. Paul Garber, Head Curator of the National Air Museum.

A man's voice said, "Paul? This is Charles."

"Charles?"

"Charles Lindbergh."

"Oh, yes, Colonel. How are you? What can I do for you?"

"I want to come down there and get into the cockpit of the *Spirit.* Is that possible?"

"Of course. It's your plane. I'll be glad to arrange it."

"Now don't go to any trouble," Lindbergh said. "We can just throw a rope up over the ship and I'll shinny up to it."

The rope wasn't necessary. Mr. Garber had a ladder ready for the colonel when he arrived, and after the museum was closed for the day Lindbergh went up the ladder and climbed into the cockpit of the little plane that made him world-famous.

"I decided that he might want to be all alone," Mr. Garber told me, "so I went to another part of the hall and sat on a bench. I guess he spent half an hour or more in the aircraft. Suddenly I heard him call, 'Paul! Come on up here!' I had seen the plane every day, but looking up and seeing Colonel Lindbergh's face smiling at me from the cockpit really gave me quite a thrill."

Mr. Garber climbed the ladder and joined Lindbergh in the cramped cockpit. Lindbergh explained that he was writing a book and that a motion picture was to be made about his historic flight, and for authenticity he needed to refresh his memory concerning the number of some tally marks he had made near his instrument panel.

The plane had five gasoline tanks. All fuel flowed into a compound-mixing chamber, called the "Lunkenheimer," and passed into the carburetor. During his flight if Lindbergh fed all the gasoline from the right-hand tank, the ship would be wing-heavy on one side. If some other tank were drained before the rest, another part of the ship would be out of balance. To keep all five tanks at the same approximate weight he fed fuel from one for a certain number of minutes, then cut it off and opened another. Each time he did this he made a vertical pencil mark on his panel, with every fifth tally a slanting line drawn through the other four ($\cancel{||||}$). To see and count these marks was the reason why he wanted to sit in the cockpit again, and he probably relived many of the exciting moments of his 33½-hour flight in 1927.

It was Paul Garber's foresight that brought the *Spirit of St. Louis* to the Smithsonian. When Lindbergh took off for Paris on May 20, 1927, his flight would be about the thirteenth across the North or South Atlantic; but the others were "island hoppers," and if Lindbergh succeeded he would be the first to fly from the mainland of the United States to the mainland of Europe.

When he was well on his way, Paul Garber suggested that the Secretary of the Smithsonian send a cablegram of congratulations to Lindy and at the same time ask him if the Smithsonian might have his airplane for posterity. The message was awaiting Lindbergh when he landed at LeBourget Field, but the request for the plane was only one of hundreds that came from industrial firms, department stores, museums and other places. One urgent plea came from the authorities in the City of St. Louis.

"Why did he choose to give it to the Smithsonian?" I asked.

"I don't really know," Mr. Garber said. "I think, however, that he considered the name Smithsonian the same way we think of the word 'Sterling' on silver."

The plane was flown to Washington by Lindbergh himself on April 30, 1928, after he had flown it to 63 cities in 48 states, to Mexico and Central and South America. It was put on display in the Smithsonian on May 8, when 36,000 visitors crowded in to see it, and it has been there ever since.

Paul Garber's interest in aviation dates from his boyhood. When he was sixteen he made a model of a Chanute glider and flew it as a kite. He thought, If I could make this big enough I could fly in it. He made a big-scale glider in his basement and assembled it in a vacant lot near his Washington, D.C., home, then recruited his teen-age friends to collect lengths of clothesline from the neighbors for use in towing the ship.

With the ropes tied together and attached to the nose of the glider, Garber climbed in and gave the signal to his friends to start running with the towline. The plane bounced over the ground, lifted and pointed toward the clouds. The rope pullers were so astonished that they stopped running before the ship was really air-borne, and it plummeted to earth tail-first.

Paul soon repaired it and they tried again, with instructions to keep running until the glider flew. And fly it did!

"I guess I sailed to an altitude of about sixty feet," he told me, "but it sure looked like a mile to me! Then for some reason we headed down and glided into a rose garden in the back yard of a house at California Street and Massachusetts Avenue. I wasn't hurt, but the rosebushes were ruined. The woman who lived there came out when she heard the commotion. She turned out to be the famous novelist Mary Roberts Rinehart, and she was really very nice about the whole thing."

Years later Garber was invited to join the Early Birds, an organization of pilots who had made solo flights before December 17, 1916. To prove that he was eligible he obtained a letter from Mrs. Rinehart attesting to the glider flight in which he used her garden as a landing field.

The date of December 17, governing membership in the Early Birds, was established because it was on December 17, 1903, that Wilbur and Orville Wright made the first successful powered flight in a manned airplane. This very same aircraft is on display in the Arts and Industries Building, but there was a time when a controversy threatened to forestall the Smithsonian's acquisition of the Kitty Hawk flyer.

In 1903, when the Wrights were experimenting with their plane, Dr. Samuel Pierpont Langley, then Secretary of the Smithsonian, was also working on a man-carrying powered aircraft of his own design which he called the Langley "aerodrome." He built and tested miniature models (wing span 14 feet) of his plane, which flew some three-fourths of a mile in one and one-half minutes. Since the design seemed to be satisfactory, a full-scale aerodrome was built and readied for a test on October 7, 1903. It was to be launched from a catapult aboard a houseboat on the Potomac River, at first without a pilot. In this launching a fitting caught on the track and caused the ship to nose into the water.

It was repaired and tested again on December 8, 1903, but the swift take-off damaged the rear stabilizer and the aircraft swooped up and over and again fell into the river. Nine days later, on December 17, the Wright brothers' plane flew at Kitty Hawk, North Carolina.

Langley's machine was taken out of the water after the second failure, dried off, and its parts were stored as the joint property of the War Department and the Smithsonian. In 1913 Dr. Langley's successor as Secretary felt that the progress of American aviation was behind that of Europe, and he established the Langley Aeronautical Laboratory to develop scientific principles for improved flight.

As one project it was decided to take the Langley aerodrome out of storage and resume tests. The parts were delivered to aviation expert Glenn Curtiss, who assembled them; but instead of using a catapult he attached floats for water launching and used a different system of guy wires for the wings. In 1914 the aerodrome was successfully flown with a pilot aboard.

The Smithsonian published a description of the 1914 test flights. At that time Orville Wright's company was engaged in a legal battle with Glenn Curtiss involving certain aircraft controls; and it was argued that Curtiss might have gained a legal advantage by demonstrating that the Langley machine could fly, because then he would have evidence of a successful aircraft that preceded the Wright plane.

After the 1914 flights the aerodrome was returned to the Smithsonian and restored to its 1903 condition, and in 1918 it was exhibited in the museum with a label reading:

ORIGINAL LANGLEY FLYING MACHINE, 1903

The first man-carrying aeroplane in the history of the world capable of sustained free flight. Invented, built and tested over the Potomac River by Samuel Pierpont Langley in 1903. Successfully flown at Hammondsport, N. Y., June 2, 1914. Dimensions: 55 feet long, 48 feet wide; sustaining wing surface, 1,040 square feet.

Orville Wright protested the wording of the first sentence of this label. This, together with the Curtiss tests, induced him to lend the Kitty Hawk flyer to the South Kensington Museum in London with the understanding that it could be recalled.

A later Secretary of the Smithsonian, Dr. Charles G. Abbot, hoped to dissolve the differences and obtain the Wright plane for the museum. He had extensive meetings and correspondence with Orville Wright, and on September 29, 1928, Dr. Abbot published a paper, *The Relations Between the Smith-*

sonian Institution and the Wright Brothers. The substance of
the bulletin was that the Wright Kitty Hawk flyer was the first
powered aircraft to achieve sustained flight with a man aboard.

Subsequently Orville Wright was also invited to write a
paper for publication by the Smithsonian (*The Langley Aerodrome of 1914*), setting out in two columns his description of
the Langley machine of 1903 and the plane as revised by
Curtiss in 1914. He told how the ship was changed and ex-
pressed his belief that aerodynamic alterations were made that
embodied improvements not available to Dr. Langley in 1903
and which brought about the later successful flight.

With the publication of these papers the differences were
resolved and Mr. Wright agreed to give the Kitty Hawk flyer
to the Smithsonian.

One impartial committee reported: "There is no question but
that the Wrights were the first to navigate the air, thus reaching
the goal long sought by many; but in our opinion when Langley's 1903 machine was wrecked in launching, he too, after
years of effort, following a different road, was in sight of the
same goal. He was like the prophet of old who, after forty
years of wandering in the wilderness, was permitted to view
the promised land upon which he never set his foot. Langley's
accomplishments in aeronautics were notable and he is entitled
to full credit for them."

World War II delayed the return of the Kitty Hawk flyer to
the United States; but when the war ended and Paul Garber
finished his tour of duty as a Commander in the Navy, he was
assigned to get the Wright plane from England. It was crated
in the original boxes and brought overseas by the Director of
the South Kensington Museum aboard the liner *Mauretania.*
Garber was to meet the ship in New York; but when he went
there he discovered that because of a dock strike the steamship
was heading for Halifax, Nova Scotia, a British port.

"At the dock I received two telegrams," he recalled with a

grin. "One said GO TO HALIFAX and the other said PLEASE CALL ST. PETER and gave a phone number." Mr. St. Peter was public information officer for the Wright Aeronautical Corporation and he asked if Mr. Garber could bring the aircraft to their factory en route to Washington. Garber agreed.

Garber then called his superiors and was told to do whatever was necessary. He arranged for a Navy truck to stand by in New York, then took a train to Montreal and flew to Halifax, where the *Mauretania* was just docking. At the dock he met Director Shaw of the English museum, who gave him the custody of the precious crates and who then left for New York.

The three big boxes were unloaded and placed under a warehouse shed. How was he going to get them to Washington? Garber telephoned Admiral A. M. Pride at the Navy Department in Washington, asking for assistance. Some three hours later the admiral called back saying that the aircraft carrier *Palau* was in the Halifax area on maneuvers and would pick him up in a few days.

For four bitterly cold days Paul Garber sat on the boxes at the warehouse, watching for the ship. "When she finally arrived, and I looked out and saw our flag waving on the *Palau*, I cried," Garber recalls. "I remember that the tears froze on my face."

As the carrier came to anchor, salutes were fired from its guns and from the guns of anchored Canadian warships. "They weren't for me," Garber said. "The royal baby had just been born!"

As each of his precious crates was slung upward by a crane, Paul Garber shivered to think what would happen if a cable should break and plunge the cargo into the sea. But the transfer was made safely and the *Palau* carried the boxes and Garber to Bayonne, New Jersey, where the Navy truck was waiting with a sign OPERATION HOMECOMING. The men aboard the carrier had also made a sign: "This is the crane that first raised the Kitty Hawk from foreign soil onto an American ship and returned it to its native land."

The ship's band played; newspaper reporters and photographers came aboard, and a police escort accompanied the loaded truck to New York. The crates were unloaded in Washington late in November and assembly of the plane began under Garber's expert supervision. It was first displayed on December 15, 1948.

A message was sent to Colonel Lindbergh asking whether or not he would object if his *Spirit of St. Louis* was placed immediately behind the Kitty Hawk flyer. Lindbergh replied that he was honored to know that his ship would share the same hall with the Wright brothers' plane.

Today the Kitty Hawk flyer is one of more than 200 historic aircraft in the collection of the National Air Museum; only 19 of them were on public view as this was written. Space limitations make impossible the display of more aircraft; but existing plans call for the construction of a new building to house the exhibits of the National Air Museum, and within a few years this part of the Smithsonian will be able to show visitors the whole story of American aviation. As of 1961, however, the Air Museum was still housed in a World War I hangar erected as a "temporary" structure in 1917!

Among the displays in the new National Air Museum will be the *Enola Gay*, the plane that made the historic 1945 flight over Hiroshima, Japan, carrying the first atomic bomb used in warfare. This ship, with three other flying warriors of World War II, was presented to the Smithsonian by the Air Force in August, 1960, and all four were placed in a Smithsonian warehouse for renovation.

Renovation involves much hard work, for the planes had been sitting in the open for years. Wings and fuselages had rusted, wood had deteriorated, upholstery was torn and birds had built nests in the interiors. Smithsonian workmen, using chemical cleaners, paint, sandblasting, woodworking and sewing equipment, will restore the planes to running order, not only to provide interest for eventual sightseers but also for the information of students of aeronautical engineering.

Engineering students should also be interested in the Bell XP-59A ("X" for Experimental, "P" for Pursuit), for this was the first jet-powered airplane built and flown in America. First flown on October 1, 1942, this ship had a ceiling of 40,000 feet and reached a speed of 400 miles per hour. It was presented to the Smithsonian in June, 1945.

The history-making Bell X-1, first rocket-powered Air Force plane and the first to fly faster than the speed of sound (October 17, 1947), is a prize exhibit of the Air Museum.

In October, 1960, the XF8U-1 (the "One-X") Crusader, the plane that spawned a new generation of Navy jet fighters, was presented to the Air Museum by its makers, Chance Vought Aircraft, Inc., of Dallas, Texas. Crusaders that followed this experimental model set the first national speed record in excess of 1000 miles per hour, became the first to span the nation faster than the speed of sound and won the Collier Trophy as an outstanding aviation achievement.

The Crusader will find itself in distinguished company in the Air Museum, sharing space with Wiley Post's globe-circling *Winnie Mae*; the Wright *Vin Fiz*, first plane to fly across the United States; the NC-4, first transatlantic plane; the Douglas cruiser *Chicago*, which flew around the world; and the V-173 *Flying Pancake*, an experimental approach to vertical take-off and landing aircraft. In addition there are several World War II German, Japanese and Italian planes.

Souvenirs of the feats of famous fliers include many of Lindbergh's personal possessions carried on his historic ocean hop; a cap worn by the late Rear Admiral Richard E. Byrd over the North Pole; the cocked hat and epaulettes of Captain Stanford Moses, first captain of the first American aircraft carrier;

and the propeller from the seaplane in which Glenn L. Martin made the first long overwater flight.

Another historic addition was made in October, 1960, when the Air Force presented the Smithsonian with the RVX 1-5, the first re-entry nose cone recovered after a missile flight into outer space. Resembling a five-foot artillery shell, the nose cone was sent to a Maryland warehouse to have spots of rust removed and to be prepared for display in the Air Museum.

More American aviation history is made vivid by such things as Captain Eddie Rickenbacker's World War I uniform and the Medal of Honor presented to him as America's Ace of Aces; by an insigne cut by Lieutenant Frank Luke, the "Balloon Buster," from a German plane he downed in combat; and by the *Swoose*, whose story typifies the bravery and ingenuity of American airmen in World War II.

The *Swoose* was born in the heat of battle. Her number, 40-3097, identifies her origin: "40" shows that she was accepted for service in 1940; "3097" was her number in a production lot of B-17-D's—"B" for Bomber, "17" for the seventeenth bomber type listed by the Air Force, and "D" for the fourth modification of that type. This Boeing plane was hailed as the fastest and longest-range bomber in the world and eventually became known as the Flying Fortress.

On December 7, 1941, the Japanese bombed Pearl Harbor in Hawaii and Clark Field at Luzon, crippling all American bombing planes at Clark Field. Continuing this story, Paul Garber has written:

By heroic efforts, finding a wing of one and a rudder from another, a tailplane from a ruined fuselage, and such engines as remained whole, and putting these odd parts together on fuselages less damaged than others, our men assembled a very few bombers. It was from such Phoenix-like resurrections that the *Swoose* came into being. Lt. Col. Hank Godman is recorded as the first to have piloted this bomber. . . . It was at Newcastle, New South Wales,

Australia, in March, 1942, according to Capt. Weldon H. Smith, then her pilot, that this relic was christened the *Swoose* shortly after it had acquired a different tail assembly, less bullet-damaged than its own, from a plane that Lieutenant George E. Schaetzel had flown in so full of holes that it had to be written off. Even with this new tail the other parts were so pieced together and battle-scarred that the airplane little resembled the beautiful Flying Fortress that had landed in the Philippines a few months before. So, being neither swan nor goose, it became the *Swoose*, and below its insigne of an odd-looking bird, painted on its fuselage, the artist added the words, 'It Flies,' as if to assure the incredulous that it could still carry on.

After scores of heroic flights the *Swoose* was flown from Australia to Washington, D.C., carrying General George H. Brett and piloted by Captain (now Colonel) Frank Kurtz, and this pieced-together ship set new speed records between Australia and Hawaii and from there to San Francisco. After four thousand hours in the air it was still in service when the war ended.

The *Swoose* was later scheduled to be scrapped and melted into raw metals; but it was rescued by Mayor Fletcher Bowron of Los Angeles, was acclaimed as a war memorial and in 1949 was presented to the National Air Museum by the City of Los Angeles. Members of her wartime crew were gathered from various cities and flew her east, piloted by Colonel Kurtz, with Paul Garber of the Smithsonian as his proud copilot.

In 1960 the *Swoose* was in storage in Washington, awaiting construction of the new Air Museum where she will be given due homage.

The story of the *Swoose* is only one of many exciting and dramatic true accounts described by Paul Garber in an illustrated Smithsonian booklet called *The National Aeronautical Collections*, for sale by the Institution.

Opposite the entrance to the Air Museum stand two giant

ballistic missiles, an Atlas, and a Jupiter-C, symbols of man's growing destructive power and also his efforts to uncover the secrets of other worlds in outer space. Helping in the search for this knowledge is a bureau of the Smithsonian known as the Astrophysical Observatory, which, however, has many unusual interests about other things here on earth.

Chapter 10

Earthbound Space Men

THE ASTROPHYSICAL OBSERVATORY IS DIVIDED INTO TWO sections: the Division of Astrophysical Research and the Division of Radiation and Organisms. The first is concerned with the study of solar and other types of energy striking the earth, the second with the investigation of radiation as it relates to biological problems.

The Astrophysical Observatory has its scientific headquarters in Cambridge, Massachusetts, where it works closely with the Harvard College Observatory, the Massachusetts Institute of Technology and other research centers. It has a field station at Table Mountain, California, which makes observations of the sun. The Division of Radiation and Organisms is in Washington.

Director of the Observatory is Dr. Fred L. Whipple, who is also well known as a Professor of Astronomy at Harvard University.

Since all energy on earth in one form or another comes from the sun, the Smithsonian was anxious to learn everything possible about the sun's radiation and especially its effect upon plant and animal life. For this purpose the Astrophysical Observatory was established in 1890. One of its first staff members was Dr. Charles G. Abbot, who became assistant to its director, then director, later an assistant secretary and in 1928 the Secretary of the Smithsonian. Although he retired at the age of 72 and is now (in 1961) in his eighties, he continues his studies in Washington as a "research associate," and I talked with him in his tiny office on the eleventh floor of a tower in the Smithsonian Building.

Every day for more than thirty years Dr. Abbot measured the temperature of the sun on the earth. Allowing for a loss in the earth's atmosphere, he could also measure its intensity outside the atmosphere. His careful studies and observations revealed that the sun's radiation varied not more than two per cent and that this variation occurred in multiples of 273 months. He is convinced that the variation affects our weather and that his findings can be used to make reasonably accurate weather forecasts years in advance.

How did he arrive at the figure of 273 months? This is how he explains it:

"About 1933, having a long series of 10-day mean values of the solar-constant measures, I made a chart of them extending the length of my office. Standing at a distance, I sought to discover repetitions of configurations in the variations. I noted a small regular variation of slightly more than an eight-month period. Then I discovered regular periods of variation of about 11¼ months and of about 39 months. It then occurred to me to find the least number of months of which, within the errors of determination, these three periods would be approximately integral submultiples. The number 273 (7 times 39, 24 times 11¼, and 34 times 8) seemed best. This number, 273 months, recommended itself as a solar period because it is approximately twice the sunspot cycle."

Dr. Abbot has made extensive studies of weather in various regions of the country, has assembled many statistics and has written several papers to explain and support his theory that:

1. The sun's output of general radiation is variable.
2. Solar variation has a master period of about 22¾ years (273 months).

3. Solar variation has many subordinate regular periodicities, all integrally related to 273 months.

4. Solar variation affects weather importantly, irrespective of periodicities.

5. Weather responds importantly to most of the regular periodic solar variations. This, he says, is a new and powerful element in meteorology.

Dr. Abbot feels that if meteorologists could accept his proofs, governments would feel justified in supporting similar studies of temperature and precipitation at numerous stations within their borders. From such studies, maps of expected weather conditions for many years in advance could be drawn, and such maps could be of great value to many industries.

"The fly in the ointment," he adds, "seems to be that tremendous disturbances of the atmosphere, such as sometimes are caused by volcanoes or by profuse use of powerful bombs, in war and in tests, may spoil forecasts of this ambitious type."

Although the Astrophysical Observatory was originally set up to study the sun, the world race into space has created a new challenge for this Smithsonian bureau—the tracking and photographing of artificial satellites in orbit. Within the Smithsonian this program is referred to as SPOT (Satellite Precision Optical Tracking). It is carried out under a grant from the National Aeronautics and Space Administration (NASA).

The program includes three activities: photographic tracking with Baker–Nunn cameras; visual tracking by Moonwatch teams; and computing, analyzing and communicating the information collected.

The photographic tracking program has established a worldwide network of twelve optical tracking stations equipped with Baker–Nunn cameras to get highly precise photographs of the satellites. The photographic results are flashed to the Cambridge headquarters, which makes its calculations and predicts positions and times of future satellite passages.

The Baker–Nunn camera combines the skills of Dr. James G. Baker and Joseph Nunn. Dr. Baker designed the optical system (lenses, etc.), which consists of a 20-inch f/1 modified Super-Schmidt telescope with a 31-inch mirror and which can cover a circular field of 30 degrees. The camera uses 55-milli-meter film with an ASA (speed) rating of 800, which means that it is very fast. It is operated at twilight, when the sun is shining on the satellite and not on the camera. It weighs about three tons and looks something like a giant white funnel stuck into a rectangular base which pivots on an axle of the tracking mechanism.

The tracking mechanism, designed by Mr. Nunn, permits speeds ranging from zero to 7000 seconds of arc per second of time (meaning it can go from horizon to horizon in 93 sec-onds), so that the motion of the camera can match that of the satellite at any point 15 degrees or more above the horizon. If camera motion did not match satellite speed, the picture would show only a blur. The tracking mechanism permits the lens to remain focused on the satellite as though it were not moving at all. The camera takes frames at varying rates, from one per second to one every 23 seconds, and it can take between 10 and 100 individual photographs of a satellite during each transit.

Each camera is equipped with precision timing devices so that each film can record the time (to one ten-thousandth of a second), as well as the position of the satellite and the back-ground of stars.

The first Baker–Nunn camera was assembled at Organ Pass, New Mexico, in November, 1957. The other eleven are in use in Hawaii, Florida, the Netherlands Antilles, Peru, Argentina, Spain, South Africa, Iran, India, Australia and Japan. The last three named are operated by local scientists, the others by Smithsonian personnel.

Several individual achievements of the stations have been quite remarkable. In March, 1960, the station at Organ Pass photographed a satellite (1959 Eta 1) for more than 30 minutes, during which time the satellite passed over more than 5000 miles of the earth's surface, a track extending from the Pacific Ocean across the continental United States and out into the Atlantic.

One Baker–Nunn camera photographed Vanguard I, a grapefruit-sized (6-inch) spherical satellite, at a height of more than 2500 miles. This is the equivalent of photographing a shiny .30-caliber bullet in flight at a distance of 200 miles!

In August, 1959, the Australian station successfully photographed Explorer VI at a distance of 14,000 miles.

Just how do they go about photographing a satellite? The Astrophysical Observatory at Cambridge sends the tracking stations precise information concerning the orbit of the satellite, including the altitude, azimuth (angular distance east or west) and speed, and the angle at which the satellite enters the shadow of the earth.

With this information the operator computes a course on paper which will permit the camera to follow the satellite for as much as possible of a track of 130 degrees. This paper track is then set on a star globe which shows the stars around the predicted path of the satellite and lets the observer visualize the difficulties that might be involved in photographing this particular satellite, which may have a zigzag orbit. Thus he can keep his camera centered on the subject.

After the pictures are taken, the film is developed and dried in about one hour. The observers then read out the position of the satellite on the background of stars, identify the stars and fix the exact time of observation. The film is projected upon star charts, detailed maps of the sky that show the locations of stars to the eleventh magnitude—about 100 times more stars than the naked eye can see. The position of the satellite among the stars then can be measured to an accuracy of one minute (one-sixtieth of a degree) of arc.

Pinpointing a satellite in this fashion may help to prove that some of our world maps show certain places to be where they aren't! Many Pacific islands, for example, are believed to be several miles from the locations where maps show them to be, mostly because the original measurements of their positions were crude.

Very precise measurements can be made by means of tri-angulation. Suppose a Baker–Nunn camera on Island "A" were to photograph a satellite at the very instant that the same satellite was being photographed by a similar camera on far-away Island "B." The exact distance from each camera to the satellite is known. By computing the length of the base of the triangle the distance from "A" to "B" could be measured exactly.

In October, 1960, the Astrophysical Observatory was conducting experiments with mechanical and electronic devices that will make it possible for two cameras, hundreds or thousands of miles apart, to photograph one satellite at precisely the same instant, allowing a margin of not more than one one-thousandth of a second. When plans and experiments are completed, work will begin to measure distances and to map earthly locations where they ought to be instead of where they now appear to be.

In the "Moonwatch" (visual observing) program, observers look through telescopes to "acquire" (locate) a satellite during its first few revolutions after blast-off. From their reports the computing experts can predict an orbit accurately enough for the Baker–Nunn camera stations to photograph the object. "Moonwatchers" also search for "lost" satellites when necessary, monitor satellites to provide corrections in orbit or speed, and track the satellites during final stages of their descent.

In 1960 there were 218 Moonwatch teams spread throughout the world, manned entirely by 5000 volunteers.

The facts accumulated since the beginning of these combined programs are providing a more detailed understanding of the effects on the earth of solar ultraviolet light, cosmic and solar X rays and other particle radiations; the physics of the upper atmosphere as it relates to more accurate weather forecasting; the points in the upper atmosphere at which energy is either absorbed or radiated; and the atmospheric disturbances caused by solar flares and solar radiation.

One other activity of the Observatory that has produced interesting results is its research on meteors and comets. Under Dr. Whipple's direction the Observatory collects micrometeoric dust—tiny particles floating high above the earth. The collecting is done by filters mounted on a Boeing B-52 high-flying jet aircraft. The dust particles trapped by the filters are examined under microscopes and have been identified and counted. Those which might be from meteors have been set aside for analysis, some have been analyzed chemically and others will be used in a study of contamination problems.

Late in 1960 Dr. Whipple told an Air Force space conference that there is a dense cloud of dust around the earth about 80 miles out, consisting of particles so small that it would take about 300 billion to make a single ounce. It is his theory that these originate as small fragments of comets and that as they approach the earth they pick up electrical charges that make them burst like bubbles into pieces so small that an individual particle would be invisible. If a manned capsule were shot into space it is probable that the particles in this immense dust cloud would sound like a drum roll as they struck the space ship, and although they may cause no physical damage Dr. Whipple suggests that passenger-carrying space vehicles be shielded with an outer metal coating so that their pilots will not be unnerved by the *rat-a-tat-tat* of the cosmic dust.

The other part of the Astrophysical Observatory, the Division of Radiation and Organisms, deals with more down-to-earth problems of solar radiation.

Chief W. H. Klein explained that the division does fundamental biological research concerning the effect of solar radiation on living organisms.

By a process known as photosynthesis a green plant absorbs radiant energy from the sun and converts it to chemical energy in the form of sugar, the basic food supply for both plants and animals. Light controls the normal growth and behavior of plants in other ways. The development of the green color in plants, the flowering and eventual production of fruits and seeds, and the structure of the plant are governed by light.

In addition to the effects of sunlight there are other radiation effects caused by such high-energy radiations as cosmic rays, X rays and radiations originating in the nucleus of atoms. These cause hereditary changes and the destruction of various biological substances, and although much research has been done in these areas the actual biochemical mechanisms are not yet completely understood in any of them.

"We use living material to study the responses of organisms to the influences of light," Dr. Klein told me. "We're interested in two things. If radiant energy is to be used it must be first absorbed. To be absorbed there must be an absorbing material, which is colored. How is the energy transferred and utilized by the growth mechanism, and what types of pigment absorb the energy? In photosynthesis we know that chlorophyll is the material that changes radiant energy into a chemical form of energy, but in various other plant responses we aren't sure what the absorbing pigment is. We have a group known as 'blue light reactions' in which we know the pigment is yellow. This could be riboflavin or one of the other yellow pigments usually found in plants."

If you have a plant in your window at home, you know that the plant usually bends toward the direction from which the light comes. If light came only from overhead the plant would grow straight up. This response of a plant to light is called *phototropism*. Oddly enough, the growth of the side of the plant facing the light may be inhibited, while the side away from the light is either normal or stimulated, although scientists differ on this point.

Some of their experiments were shown to me by Victor B. Elstad, a plant physiologist in this division. The effects of light were clearly visible on a legume plant growing in artificial light. If the light is turned out the plant promptly folds up its leaves, and opens them again when the light is turned on.

"We want to find out what causes this," Mr. Elstad told me. "As yet we don't know too much about it. Some plants have a pulvinus, a small structure at the base of the petiole (the stem between the leaf and the main stem). Normally the pulvinus works by osmosis (the tendency of fluids to go through a porous substance), and it has to do mainly with water. When water is in the stem it extends, making the leaf move upward or outward and open. When the leaf folds there is a loss of water for some reason."

The cause of flowering by light was discovered about 1917 by two experts in the Department of Agriculture who learned that daylight influences flowers. Plants bloomed in spring, summer and fall, but no one knew definitely what caused them to flower until these two men found that the length of daylight would determine whether a plant would bloom or not.

"Roughly we group plants into three categories," Mr. Elstad said, "short-day plants, which will flower when the day is short; long-day, when the day is long; and day-neutral or indeterminate, which pays no attention to day length. The tomato, for instance, is a day-neutral that will flower and produce fruit which will enlarge for a certain length of time and will flower again in spring, summer and fall. In most cases, however, a difference of one-half a day of daylight will be the difference between a plant flowering or not flowering."

He showed me one group of poinsettias and said, "These plants would ordinarily flower on December tenth; but we want them to be in full bloom at Christmas time, so we control the light to make sure they will flower on December twentieth."

The poinsettia is a "short-day" plant, which means that if it gets "long-day" light its flowering will be delayed. Therefore, Mr. Elstad rigged an electric light to be automatically turned on at midnight and off at 1:00 A.M. from September 22 to October 10. This is the equivalent of lengthening the day, and from experience he knew that this much extra light would postpone the flowering until December 20.

What causes a plant to flower is the energy absorbed from light by the leaves, but the substance that produces the flowering is what Mr. Elstad and his associates are trying to identify. The flower actually forms before it is visible, just as the leaves which will come out on the trees next spring were really formed *last* spring!

One experiment designed to shed light on the pigment associated with flowering responses deals with the study of white and yellow mutant sunflowers. When exposed to light these sunflowers develop and grow normally except that they do not form chlorophyll, or green coloring. Use of these plants, therefore, should provide a tool to study the pigment associated with flowering in the absence of extraneous pigmented substances such as the chlorophyll.

In a building adjoining the greenhouse Mr. Elstad showed me his "growth chambers," in which experimental plants are grown entirely by artificial light. The chambers are wooden cabinets in which temperature and humidity are controlled. In the top of each cabinet are fifteen 15-watt fluorescent tubes, with four incandescent lights above them. The lights are on only during normal daylight hours.

In one of these chambers I saw a barley plant which had grown to maturity, with its golden grain ready to harvest. This was planted on July 14, and we looked at it on October 8. In the next cabinet was another barley plant which was also planted on July 14, but it was still green and had no head or flower. I was puzzled by the great difference until Mr. Elstad called my attention to the lighting. In the cabinet with the matured grain all 15 fluorescent bulbs and the four incandescent bulbs were lighted; but in the chamber with the green plant only the fluorescents were turned on, and none of the four incandescents.

"The incandescent lights provide what we call far-red light," he explained. "This is the kind of light that helps to control the flowering."

Both the fluorescent and incandescent lights have blue and red wave lengths; but in addition the incandescents have far-red, which is close to the invisible end of the spectrum.

It is by experiments such as those conducted by the Division of Radiation and Organisms that scientists hope to discover biological principles that will enable man to control, change and improve his environment. On these principles, progress in many fields, such as medicine, agriculture, nutrition and radiation protection, is dependent.

Chapter 11

Hark to the Past

AT THE ENTRANCE TO A CEMETERY IN EVERETT, MASSA-
chusetts, stood an old two-story house that a florist used as a
workshop for potting plants and flowers.

One day Dr. and Mrs. Arthur M. Greenwood of Marlboro,
Massachusetts, saw this building and recognized it as an example of architecture in the Massachusetts Bay Colony in the late
1600s. The Greenwoods themselves lived in a seventeenth-
century home in Marlboro.

Mrs. Greenwood learned that the house was built originally
by a weaver, who sold it within a few years to a bricklayer.
Both men were also farmers, since nearly every family had to
grow its own food in those early days. Eventually the house
was bought by the florist for use as a potting shop, and Mrs.
Greenwood bought it and arranged to have it moved to her
estate in Marlboro.

Like other frame houses of its day it was built with wooden
pins, ship-fashion, and could be taken apart in sections. The
timbers used in the house had been cut in the forests and
hand-shaped to fit; so it was a simple matter to mark each one
before it was dismantled, showing its position in the house. In
this way the building was moved to the Greenwood grounds

127

in Marlboro and reassembled, and there it stayed for some thirty years.

In the 1950s C. M. Watkins, Acting Curator of the Smithsonian's Division of Cultural History, searched for a specimen of a kitchen used in a seventeenth-century home. He had no luck until he went to Mrs. Greenwood and told her about his quest. Perhaps she would let the Smithsonian have the kitchen of the house she moved from Everett?

"Why take just the kitchen?" she asked. "Why not take the whole house?"

Mr. Watkins was overjoyed, but he could not accept such a gift without consulting his associates. He chuckled as he told me this story. "When I said I wanted to accept a whole two-story house for the museum, I think some of my colleagues thought I was out of my mind! But we accepted it anyway."

The house was dismantled again, moved to Washington and rebuilt in the Hall of Everyday Life in Early America—in the Museum of Natural History, where it attracts much attention. Although visitors may not go into the house, glass panels are so arranged that one may see everything in the two downstairs rooms and the method of construction upstairs. By flicking a switch near the door the spectator can see what the interior was like at night (with candlelight) and by day.

Recreating the surroundings of our forefathers, preserving relics of American history and culture, making us aware of our American heritage, these are the purposes of the Department of Civil History. Its activities are divided into four sections: The Division of Political History, Division of Cultural History, Division of Philately and Postal History, and the Division of Numismatics.

In the Hall of Everyday Life in Early America your imagination can almost bring to life the people who once lived in the rooms you see, and who used the tools and cooking utensils and other objects on display. There is a one-room schoolhouse (in Massachusetts public schools were required by law as early as 1647) in which you can almost hear the voices of children; and you'll smile at the two signs in the room, one reading LOVE ONE ANOTHER, and the other SWEAR NOT AT ALL.

One case shows the four early settlements—Jamestown (1607), Plymouth (1620), Salem (1630) and New Amsterdam (1624)—in miniature, and a recording explains the significance of each.

Church attendance was practically compulsory and one display shows a tithing rod, used by "tithing men" to keep order and to poke any bored churchgoer who happened to doze off. A huge hourglass was used "to measure sermons barely endurable in length."

Indians roamed the settlements, some collecting scalps, some making arrowheads, some trapping and trading furs—all on view.

Iron was scarce, and the few nails like those on exhibit were hand-made and used sparingly.

Today we flick a switch and see our homes flooded with electric light, a great contrast to the lighting devices used in early America, which included grease lamps, candles, whale oil lamps and tin lanterns. Mr. Watkins told me that the Smithsonian has one of the world's largest collections of lighting devices.

People ate simple foods and drank beer and cider with their meals. The beer was homemade. One governor, writing about Virginians in 1670, said, "The poorer sort brew their beer with molasses and bran; with Indian corn malted with drying in a stove; with persimmons dried in a cake and baked." Nearly everyone, from infants to graybeards, drank hard cider at home, at funerals, weddings, parties, vestry meetings and barn raisings—along with coffee, tea, milk and water.

All of these exhibits represent only a fraction of the 15,000 specimens in the research collection of the Division of Cultural

History. With Anthony W. Hathaway, an associate of Mr. Watkins, I looked at many of the specimens filed away for reference. Cabinets fitted with trays like drawers held scores of lighting devices, pottery and silver. One case was filled with harpoons, lances and other whaling instruments. There were old greeting cards, twin photographs for old-fashioned stereoscopes, framed pictures, mirrors and a variety of mechanical coin banks.

In one drawer marked "Cowboy Outfits" we found a pair of brown leather chaps that had obviously been worn long and hard by some broncobuster. There were also a pair of black fur-covered chaps, a buckskin jacket and a wolfskin rug.

In one hall were rows of pianos, harpsichords, music boxes, horns, violins, old organs and other musical instruments of Europe and America. Most of the piano collection was donated by Washington piano dealer Hugo Worch. One specimen that captured my fancy was about one-fourth the size of an ordinary grand piano. It was painted black and stood on a low black platform. The keys were not more than half an inch wide, so that an average man or woman would find it difficult to avoid striking two keys at once with one finger. I learned later from J. D. Shortridge, Associate Curator, that this midget grand, made by the Kirkman Piano Company, had been used by the famous General Tom Thumb, ballyhooed by P. T. Barnum as the smallest man in the world (his real name was Charles Stratton and he was 31 inches tall).

Pianos not more than three inches long are part of the miniature furnishings in a remarkable "Doll House" which shows how a well-to-do American family lived at the beginning of the twentieth century. In 1887 a four-room doll house was presented as a plaything to Miss Faith Bradford. It became a beloved toy and Miss Bradford added both rooms and tiny furnishings until she had a ten-room mansion filled with wonderful scale models of chairs, tables, mirrors and other accessories, bathroom fixtures, stove—and people and pets.

The "people" were "Peter Doll and his wife, Rose Washington Doll, and their children, including two sets of twins. Grandmother and Grandfather Doll are honored guests of the family. Each member of the family has his own pet and some have several. The Dolls have five servants—a nurse, a butler, a parlor maid, a chambermaid and a cook."

A wooden platform in front of the doll house is well worn by the footsteps of thousands of boys and girls (and grownups) who crowd in yearly to marvel at this tiny home of long ago.

Great care is taken to preserve all the treasures in the historical collections. The Smithsonian has a "fumatorium," a huge chamber in which furniture and other objects, including stuffed birds and animals, are placed when they are received. The chamber is filled with a lethal gas which will kill insects that may infest the specimens. One most unwelcome guest is the powder-post beetle, which produces a powdery pile of sawdust by eating holes in wood.

Metal objects come in for careful treatment. Many which are rusty when received are treated with acid or lye to remove the rust, then covered with special protective lacquer.

Furniture is polished with a mixture of oil and turpentine which must be applied about every two or three months.

In the Department of Civil History I talked with Associate Curator Peter C. Welsh, who was in the midst of research for an exhibit hall to be installed in the new Museum of History and Technology—to be called "The Growth of the United States." Using various specimens from other historical divisions of the Smithsonian, the new hall will depict the growth of our country from 1640 or earlier through 1945 or later. One section will deal with very recent developments and will be changed from time to time as necessary. The rest of the hall will be divided into 100-year segments, each showing a complete cultural development—science, family life, industry, the arts, economics and some of the more difficult subjects such as politics and law—the entire story of American progress.

"No other museum in the United States currently has an exhibit of the kind we plan for The Growth of the United States," Mr. Welsh told me.

One of the prize possessions of the Smithsonian is the portable desk used by Thomas Jefferson when he drafted the Declaration of Independence. In 1775 and 1776 Jefferson attended the Continental Congress, then meeting in Philadelphia. While there he boarded at the home of Benjamin Randolph, an expert cabinetmaker, from whom he ordered the desk which Jefferson himself designed.

The closed desk is 9¾ inches long, 14⅜ inches wide and 3¼ inches deep. The length seems short, but there is a hinged board on the desk top which opens to make the surface almost 20 inches long. The folding board is lined with green baize (heavy woolen cloth). There is a long drawer, 1¾ inches deep, divided into sections to hold paper and pens, and a compartment holding a small hand-blown glass inkwell. The drawer is fitted with a lock and keyhole, and with a handle which also serves for carrying the whole desk.

There is a row of five notches along each side of the stationary top and an easel-like structure on the back of the hinged board. The legs of the easel may be fitted into any of the notches to raise or lower the board to suit the comfort of the user.

Jefferson carried the desk with him frequently and used it in the writing of much personal correspondence. In 1825 he made a gift of the desk to Joseph Coolidge of Boston, his grandson-in-law, and under the writing board on the desk itself Jefferson attached this statement in his own handwriting:

Th. Jefferson gives this Writing Desk to Joseph Coolidge, junr. as a memorial of affection. It was made from a drawing of his own, by Ben Randall [Jefferson apparently forgot the name was Randolph], cabinet maker of Philadelphia, with whom he first lodged on his arrival in that city in May, 1776 and is the identical one on which he wrote the Declaration of Independence. Politics as well as Religion has its superstitions, these, gaining strength with time, may, one day, give imaginary value to this relic, for its association with the birth of the Great Charter of our Independence, Monticello. Nov. 18, 1825.

For the next fifty years the desk remained in the Coolidge family and, as predicted by Jefferson, it became famous as a historical treasure. In 1880 the Coolidge children gave the desk to the United States and it was exhibited in the Department of State along with the original Declaration of Independence. In 1921 the State Department, by order of the President, gave the Declaration to the Library of Congress and sent the Jefferson desk to the Smithsonian. Then the surprises began!

In 1925 American newspapers carried a front-page story saying that the Bismarck Museum in Berlin, Germany, had on display the original desk on which Jefferson wrote the Declaration of Independence. The story said that the desk was given to Prince Otto von Bismarck as an 81st birthday present by Thomas Jefferson Coolidge, son of Joseph Coolidge, Jr., who was United States Minister to France from 1892 to 1896. The American public clamored to have this priceless treasure returned to the United States, and it was reported that the Bismarck family would part with the desk—for a price. At this stage a Jefferson expert announced that the United States government already owned the original desk and that the one in Berlin was obviously a copy.

The publicity served to root out other imitations. One belonged to a doctor in Berryville, Virginia, who was sure his was the original because it had been presented to him by a patient whose family had owned it for many years. However, the drawer opened on the opposite side from that in the origi-

nal, and instead of green baize the wood was covered with red
felt.

Another replica, once believed to be the original, was in
Jefferson's Monticello at Charlottesville, Virginia.

The Smithsonian experts were able to examine one copy
when it was brought to them in the 1950s for comparison with
the original. At first there seemed to be little or no difference
between the two; but close inspection showed that the wood of
the original was darker, and the hinges, screws and lock did
not match the handmade fittings of the museum desk. The
manuscript in Jefferson's handwriting seemed to be exactly
the same on the copy as on the original. This desk had come
from an old New England family that had assumed it was the
real thing.

Where did all the imitations come from? In her report as
Associate Curator of the Department of Civil History, Mrs.
Margaret W. Brown Klapthor suggested:

Making souvenir relics of the founders of our country was a
well-established practice throughout the nineteenth century. It was
especially popular about the time of the centennial celebration of
the signing of the Declaration of Independence in 1876, when millions of souvenirs were copied from all types of articles that had
historical associations. In view of the accuracy with which the
original desk is copied it is reasonable to believe that the Coolidge
family had reproductions of the desk made before it was turned
over to the President in 1880. It is even possible that each of the
four donors [Coolidge children] had copies of the desk made and
that more of these replicas are in existence than we suppose.

At any rate, when you see the Jefferson portable desk in the
north hall of the Arts and Industries Building (or after it is
moved to the new Museum of History and Technology), you
may be sure that you are looking at the genuine article and not
a counterfeit.

Every four years, during our national elections, there's one part of the Smithsonian that has a special attraction for visitors. That's the Hall of Political History, where one may look back for a capsule view of goings-on in other long-forgotten battles for ballots in these United States.

Chapter 12

Politics, Postage, Money and War

IN OCTOBER, 1960, WITH A PRESIDENTIAL ELECTION IN THE offing, the Hall of Political History in the Arts and Industries Building displayed posters and banners urging voters to support Abraham Lincoln and Hannibal Hamlin, and included exhibits of campaign buttons and other souvenirs of that historic period.

There is one case in which are displayed the "stovepipe" beaver hat worn by Lincoln the night he was assassinated at Ford's Theater, and the black business suit he wore earlier that day. There is an inkwell which Lincoln used, and a mahogany stand which was in his home in Springfield, Illinois, and which he sold to a neighbor, William Helmle, before Lincoln moved to the White House.

Similar relics of other political figures and parties are in the research collections and are brought out from time to time for display.

One of the division's biggest attractions is the First Ladies' Hall, in which plaster female figures are dressed in gowns worn by Presidents' wives and official hostesses (who were also known as "First Ladies"). Responsibility for the hall rests with

Mrs. Margaret B. Klapthor, Associate Curator of the Division of Political History. The hall was opened in 1955.

"The collection was started about 1909 by Mrs. Julian James and Mrs. Gouverneur Hoes," Mrs. Klapthor told me. "Mrs. James was a descendant of James Monroe and had some Monroe clothing in her possession. When they started collecting, the first gown received was the inaugural gown worn by Mrs. William Howard Taft, who was the First Lady in 1912."

Mrs. Taft's interest in the project helped them to get gowns from earlier administrations, and by 1920 they had acquired specimens dating back to Martha Washington. Since 1920 it has been customary for each First Lady to present a dress to the Smithsonian. Contrary to popular belief, not all are inaugural gowns because some of those worn in the early days have disappeared and in some cases the First Lady was not present for the inaugural ceremonies. The Woodrow Wilsons did not believe in dancing, and no inaugural balls were held from the time of Taft to that of Franklin D. Roosevelt, partly because of wars and depressions. Sometimes the Presidents, for various reasons, appointed relatives or family friends to act as "official hostesses" in place of wives, and some of the gowns on display are those worn by these substitutes.

The gowns are in a series of eight period settings which show the kind of surroundings in which they were originally worn. Much of the furniture was once used in the White House and was so badly worn that it had to be completely restored by the Smithsonian craftsmen. Every effort has been made to make each setting as much as possible like its White House counterpart. Each case displays dresses representing a time span of 25 years and shows changing styles in White House room decorations.

Martha Washington's dress is of salmon pink faille which has been hand-painted with a gray-white ribbon chain forming medallion spaces. In the medallions are painted wild flowers, grasshoppers, spiders and other insects. Martha customarily wore a "mobcap" to all social functions, and one of white lace is shown on the model.

Some other interesting sidelights are:

The bell-sleeve dress worn by Betty Taylor Bliss, daughter of President Zachary Taylor, is the last in the collection to be made entirely with hand stitching. The sewing machine was invented in 1846 and all later dresses in the collection have some machine sewing on them.

On the gown worn by Mrs. Rutherford B. Hayes, look for the Kappa Kappa Gamma sorority pin. The first college graduate to preside as First Lady, Mrs. Hayes was made an honorary member of the sorority in 1880.

Oddly enough, the gown identified with Mrs. James A. Garfield was worn by her at the inaugural ball in 1881, which was held in the very same Smithsonian building in which the dress is now displayed. Exhibits had not yet been moved into the museum.

Mrs. William McKinley was an invalid at the time of the inaugural ball and collapsed as she was standing in the great ballroom in the Pension Office. The fall made a black mark which may still be seen on the right side of her skirt.

The red dress worn by Mrs. Calvin Coolidge is the only representative of the short-dress period in the collection. Mrs. Coolidge herself put her Pi Beta Phi sorority pin on the left breast of the figure just after the gown was installed in the case.

Anyone interested in complete descriptions of the gowns and in stories about their wearers may read about them in a Smithsonian book, *Dresses of the First Ladies of the White House*, by Margaret W. Brown, which includes beautiful full-color illustrations. The book may be purchased at, or ordered by mail from, the Smithsonian Institution.

Preserving these cloth treasures is a problem. One unusual precaution is the use of specially filtered light in the display cases, since ordinary incandescent light would cause the colors to fade. Regular housekeeping chores are also required in the settings—dusting, sweeping and washing windows.

Preservation of other clothing is also of great concern to Mrs. Anne W. Murray, Assistant Curator of the Division of Political History, who has charge of American period costumes.

Mrs. Murray has a wonderful collection of period costumes which have not been displayed because no space was available, but which will be shown in a special hall of the new Museum of History and Technology.

She showed me much of her costume collection. "Costume" includes not only dresses, but also shoes, hats, gloves, underwear, jewelry, fans and umbrellas, generally classed as "accessories." One woman even donated a gold toothpick holder, worn like a fob on a watch chain by gentlemen who couldn't brush after every meal!

Other items: Handkerchief rings, worn on a finger, with a handkerchief dangling from a delicate gold chain attached to the ring.

Several gold and silver hairpins, two inscribed "Tiffany."

Two pairs of nineteenth-century black silk stockings with clocks; estimated cost, $100 per pair!

A Spencer jacket, short-waisted (like the Eisenhower jacket). This garment was named for Lord Spencer, who accidentally burned the tails off a tailcoat and decided to wear it anyway.

There is a fine collection of Quaker clothing—bonnets, shawls, aprons and dresses—and one Quaker wedding dress, which is of extremely simple design and made of gray silk.

There are no seventeenth-century costumes in the collection and not much clothing worn by men from 1820 to 1860.

"What I want most to get," Mrs. Murray said, "is *everyday* clothing worn in the seventeenth, eighteenth and nineteenth centuries. The families of those periods often preserved wedding dresses, party dresses or graduation dresses; but they simply wore out their everyday clothes, or cut them up to make clothing for children, or discarded them. This is the kind of costume I'd like to get, to show what people wore as they went about their daily business." She added, "Also, if anyone would care to give us a good quality dress typical of the 1947 'New Look,' we'd be glad to have it."

In studying costume, old paintings are important, for there were no fashion prints until the end of the eighteenth century. Some early artists were not especially concerned about the costumes of their subjects, but masters like Van Dyke, Rubens and Haller (an English engraver) have left valuable pictorial records. New European fashions were copied in miniature and put on "fashion dolls" which were shipped to America to be used as patterns by dressmakers. Fashion plates in America started with *Godey's Lady's Book* about 1830. One fashion print in Godey's showed a woman wearing gloves while eating breakfast. Soon this became a fad, but it didn't last.

The sewing machine made a great difference in costume because more people began to make their own clothes. Some men said the sewing machine was a boon because it would keep women so busy that they would forget about suffrage and the fight for women's rights. How wrong can you be?

Mrs. Murray receives all sorts of inquiries about costume. When did men begin to wear suspenders? (At the end of the eighteenth century, and they called them "braces.") How did men hold up those fancy knee pants? (They were tailored to grasp the wearer's legs firmly.) How can I preserve an old dress? (To answer this she must know the fabric used. If it is in flat storage, put it in tissue paper and avoid all creasing of material; for creases will break linen or silk.)

What about dry cleaning? The Smithsonian does not dry-clean many of its period costumes because damaging effects might show up sometime later. Some specimens, not valuable for study, have been dry-cleaned, and Mrs. Murray makes a careful record of the treatment given each—so that future curators may trace causes of damage, if any.

Damage to specimens of any kind is of great concern to all curators, but especially to Curator G. T. Turner of the Division of Philately and Postal History; for many of the rare stamps in his tremendous collection could never be replaced if they were lost or damaged.

There are about nine million specimens of stamps in the Smithsonian collection (as of 1961), and more are added regularly. One dependable source of new stamps is the Universal Postal Union (UPU), established in 1879 to meet at least once a year and to make regulations for the cooperation of various governments in postal matters.

When the United States or other member country issues a new postage stamp, a specified number of the stamps must go to the UPU headquarters in Berne, Switzerland. The UPU then sends specimens of the stamps to all of its members. The Post Office Department in Washington receives five or six stamp shipments from the UPU every year, comprising three copies of each new stamp. Two specimens are kept by the Post Office Department and the third is given to the Smithsonian for its collection.

From twenty-five hundred to thirty-five hundred stamps are issued each year by member countries of the UPU.

When new United States stamps are issued, three copies of each design are given to the Smithsonian. One United States stamp of special interest is a 1946 three-cent issue commemorating the one-hundredth anniversary of the founding of the Smithsonian Institution.

Private collectors sometimes present specimens to the Smithsonian. Occasionally the postal director of a foreign country who has visited the Smithsonian will send new issues to the museum as a courtesy.

Some stamp collections have been bequeathed to the museum by the wills of collectors.

In the Philatelic Hall are rows and rows of mahogany cases with sliding panels containing about 350,000 glass-covered specimens of stamps of every conceivable kind. Millions of specimens not on display are available to serious philatelists or scholars for research purposes. The collection will be moved to the new Museum of History and Technology when the building is completed, and there the Hall of Philately and Postal History will have exhibit space some four times greater than that used in 1961.

The research collection of stamps is kept in air-conditioned space where temperature and humidity levels are controlled. Naphthalene and other chemicals are used to prevent damage by insects.

I asked Mr. Turner and Associate Curator Frank J. McCall if their collection lacked any valuable specimens. It does.

"Many common stamps are missing from our collection," Mr. McCall said. "Among other things, we'd like to get some Postmaster Provisionals." He grinned at me. "There's one particular specimen we're hoping someone will donate to us one day. It's a one-cent stamp of 1851 known as Type One."

"Why the big grin?" I asked.

"The stamp is worth about seventy-five hundred dollars," he answered.

Money, like stamps, is of interest to millions of collectors, amateur and professional alike, and every year thousands of these numismatists visit the displays in the Smithsonian's Division of Numismatics, where I talked with Curator Vladimir Clain-Stefanelli.

"We're concerned with the history of money," Dr. Stefanelli said. "The first emphasis is on coins, because paper money is only a medium of exchange, although as a numismatist I feel that paper money is as important as coined money."

The Smithsonian collection of coins and paper money totals about 116,000 specimens, many of which are extremely rare. There are two designs of an 1877 fifty-dollar gold coin, only one or two others of which are in existence. The Smithsonian has a double-eagle (twenty-dollar gold piece) struck in 1849— the only one of its kind known to exist. There are three known 1822 five-dollar gold coins, one of which the Smithsonian has.

One coin the museum does *not* have is a 1913 Liberty Head nickel. "Only five of these particular nickels were made, apparently under unusual circumstances," Dr. Stefanelli said. "All five are owned by private collectors and there is no specimen in the United States Mint Bureau, which customarily keeps examples of all of its coins. If this particular nickel was struck officially by the mint, why was not a specimen kept? It would appear that this coin was not an official product of the government."

Dr. Stefanelli receives numerous inquiries from collectors and others. One man brought in a metallic disk bearing a design representing the sun and encrusted with dirt. He was quite excited because he believed his find was an ancient coin or perhaps one that had come from outer space! He was deflated and disappointed when Dr. Stefanelli identified the disk as an advertising novelty distributed by the makers of Solarine, a commercial cleaning product.

Many letter writers send in "rare coins" which they claim to have "found buried under four feet of earth," or under some other unusual circumstances. Generally these turn out to be pieces of "play money" or tokens packed as prizes in commercial packages.

The incoming mail still brings specimens of "Confederate bills left to me by my grandfather." Some are genuine; many are replicas that were printed as giveaways by cereal manufacturers.

One woman brought in a medal she claimed was given to a

member of her family. Dr. Stefanelli established that the medal was actually struck long after the family member died.

Only occasionally does a visitor bring in a rare coin. One Maryland woman brought in a coin which she had found near Baltimore in a very poor state of preservation. It turned out to be a copper penny which was made for Lord Baltimore in England in 1658. Up to the time of her visit only three of these coins were known to exist. Hers became the fourth.

Dr. Stefanelli gave her some advice which applies to all collectors. If an old coin is found corroded, don't attempt to clean it; for you may do more harm than good by destroying valuable characteristics. If you insist upon cleaning an old coin, use only soap and water, rub it as gently as possible and don't try to polish it.

Some visitors bring or send in Continental currency dating from American Revolutionary days. "It's still not worth a continental," Dr. Stefanelli said.

Numerous people ask the Smithsonian to tell them how much certain specimens of money are worth as collectors' items. The Smithsonian policy is never to quote prices, but to refer inquirers to standard books on numismatics, such as *A Guide Book of United States Coins*, by R. S. Yeoman, or *Paper Money of the United States*, by Robert Friedberg.

The Smithsonian has on display the largest and finest collection of foreign gold coins in the world. With all other specimens these will be moved to the new Museum of History and Technology, where the story of the evolution of money will be shown in 19 panels designed to educate and entertain every visitor from eight to eighty, collector or not.

The priceless money display is safeguarded by an elaborate electronic alarm system so sensitive that even a sharp blow on a display case or any excessive vibration will touch off an alarm and send guards rushing to the source of possible trouble.

The Smithsonian collection includes specimens of "invasion currency," used in time of war by various military forces.

Military and naval history, however, is the concern of two other divisions, the Division of Military History and the Division of Naval History, which make up the Department of Armed Forces History, headed by Mendel L. Peterson.

"Our purpose is to preserve and study any relics of the United States Armed Forces," Mr. Peterson explained. "The more we can understand about what our predecessors did, the better we can prepare ourselves for the future. We can determine what characteristics helped them to preserve the country and perhaps we can examine our own motives and characteristics in a new light. If we can make people appreciate the resourcefulness and courage and inventiveness and energy of our ancestors, who conquered the wilderness as civilians, and show that these are the qualities that built this nation, we are serving a useful purpose."

To get this idea across he displays objects, documents and illustrations in interesting fashion. "Just to look at a simple weapon that some pioneer actually used to fight his way through the wilderness gives the spectator a feeling of the great qualities of American character," Mr. Peterson said.

This is not the only purpose, however. The Smithsonian seeks to preserve for posterity, and to identify in publications and exhibits, the many technical developments in the history of our armed forces, the evaluation of weapons of war, and heraldry (flags and symbols). The Hall of Ordnance will show technical aspects, and the chronological Hall of Weapons presents exhibits from the historical point of view.

Mr. Peterson also acts as Curator of the Division of Naval History and his particular specialty is underwater exploration. He feels that the world under water is "the last great store of historical material on earth."

"A shipwreck is almost like a time capsule," he pointed out. "Everything found in it is a cross section of some particular period—weapons, tools, furniture, objects of everyday use. Everything in that capsule, once you determine it has not been contaminated, provides a collection which you can say was in use in channels of commerce in some particular year or period."

Mr. Peterson, who holds the rank of Commander in the United States Naval Reserve, saw combat service in the Pacific and was a member of Task Force 39 exploring the Antarctic in 1947–48. He has explored historic underwater sites in the Florida Straits, West Indies and Bermuda since 1952 as part of a research program in naval history.

In diving he has used SCUBA (Self-Contained Underwater Breathing Apparatus) equipment and also a "floating hose." With the floating hose a diver carries a long hose through which air is pumped from topside, and he need not be concerned about exhausting air in tanks strapped to his back as in SCUBA diving.

In one Smithsonian bulletin Mr. Peterson wrote: "The underwater shipwreck of popular fiction usually lies listing on one side, hull intact, masts erect, moss streaming from the rigging and perhaps even a skeleton at the wheel. In actuality the wreck of a wooden ship over one hundred years old is marked only by coral- or sand-covered metal objects, all exposed timber having been destroyed by the teredo shipworm. Metal remains that have lain in sea water in the southern areas of the Florida Straits are covered within a few years by a natural coral cement which appears to be formed from the corrosion products of the iron object combined with the coral sand that abounds on the sea bottom in that area. Thus it is that a shipwreck site is camouflaged by nature and takes on the exact color of its natural surroundings."

According to Mr. Peterson, "The trained diver learns quickly to detect the unnatural lines of man-made objects through the coral coating. The most prominent remains of most early shipwrecks are the barrels of the guns. Until the middle of the nineteenth century even merchant ships carried cannon as protection against pirates at sea. Lying on a shipwreck site, these cannon are signposts to the diver, who quickly learns to detect their presence even though they may be covered by masses of growing coral."

When I talked with Mr. Peterson he had recently returned from Bermuda, where he succeeded in identifying a salvaged ship as the *Sea Venture*. The *Sea Venture*, commanded by Sir George Somers, was shipwrecked in 1609, and the wreck was described by Sylvester Jourdan in an account called *A Discovery of the Bermudas*. It is believed that the story of this wreck provided William Shakespeare with the plot for his play *The Tempest*. The remains of the ship were found recently by Edmund Downing, a diver from the Bermuda Naval Air Base, who followed clues he obtained from the Bermuda government archives.

One of Mr. Peterson's projects is a study of guns and their marks and decorations, and he has photographed hundreds of guns in Europe and throughout this hemisphere. The diver or explorer who is interested in this subject must now examine hundreds of books to identify various specimens, so Mr. Peterson's findings will be set out in a field handbook which he is preparing for use by explorers. The book will contain hundreds of illustrations of objects from shipwreck sites which can be definitely dated and which will aid in dating other locations. If a diver fishes up a rum bottle, compares it to one of the pictures and finds it identical in shape and proportion to one recovered from a wreck in 1819, he will know it is of the same period.

One unusual specimen in the Smithsonian's collection is an ancient iron anchor presented by the government of Haiti in 1960. It was discovered in 1956 in the waters off Cape Haitian by Edwin A. Link, underwater explorer and inventor of the Link trainer of World War II aviation fame.

Measurements and chemical tests show that the anchor,

which looks like rotten wood, is almost identical in size (6 feet long) and of the same kind of iron as another anchor in the National Museum at Port au Prince, Haiti, which was discovered on the site of Navidad, a settlement established by Christopher Columbus in December, 1492, after the loss of his flagship, the *Santa Maria*. Mr. Peterson and other authorities believe that both anchors may have been used on the *Santa Maria*, and he is continuing research to try to establish this fact definitely.

As Head Curator of the Department of Armed Forces History, Mr. Peterson works closely with Mr. E. M. Howell, Curator of the Division of Military History, which deals with the military history of the United States and with European military history only as it influenced the development of firearms and edged weapons in America.

Many military relics are still being excavated, and Mr. Howell himself has dug up quite a few. Field work consists mostly in excavating camp sites rather than battle sites, and a few of these locations are still relatively untouched. Some of those used during the War of 1812, for example, are along the frontiers of the Great Lakes, but the specific locations are never made public for fear that amateur "pot hunters" will invade the sites and ruin specimens that are of great historical value.

Research collections include uniforms worn by soldiers in the regular army dating from 1832, but there are no specimens of uniforms worn during the American Revolution or the War of 1812. One important exhibit is the uniform worn by George Washington when he resigned his army commission.

There is a tremendous collection of weapons—ranging from a Crusader's sword from Cyprus dating from about 1150, up to firearms used in World War II or later.

"Any firearm up to the War of 1812 could be considered military," Mr. Howell said. "The Kentucky rifle, which actually originated in Pennsylvania, was used during the Revolution by Morgan's rifle companies. We don't know what kind of rifles Lewis and Clark carried when they went west, though we think some of them were 'Harpers Ferry 1803' models. We do know that they had rifles, and that one of them was an air rifle! It was invented in Europe and, although no description of it exists, it was probably like our modern air gun and used pellets as ammunition."

One big group of specimens in the collection shows military insignia, including cap plates, hat badges, shoulder-belt plates, waist-belt plates, epaulettes and buttons.

Perhaps the proudest possession of the division is the original Star-Spangled Banner that waved "in the rockets' red glare" over Fort McHenry during the British bombardment. When an officer changed his post of duty it was customary to present him with his garrison flag; and the Fort McHenry banner was thus given to Colonel Olmsted, commander of the Fort. It remained in his family until 1912, when it was lent to the Smithsonian, and several years later it was made an outright gift. In the new Museum of History and Technology the flag will be suspended from the ceiling near the entrance, a spectacular and inspiring sight to greet the millions of visitors who will enter the newest American treasure house.

The huge banner has fifteen stripes and one mystery. The mystery is a strip of red linen sewed on one white strip (tenth from the top) in the shape of an inverted "V." Nobody knows why or by whom it was put there.

Smithsonian visitors interested in military and naval history will find scores of unusual objects in the exhibition halls in the Arts and Industries Building. There is a bronze field piece brought to the United States in 1777 by General Lafayette and used by the Americans and French against the British in the American Revolution.

In one big glass case stands "Winchester," the black horse that was ridden by General Philip Sheridan through much of the Civil War. Originally named "Rienzi," the horse was called

"Winchester" after he carried Sheridan on his famous ride from Winchester, Virginia, to Cedar Creek in time to rally his troops and turn almost certain defeat into victory.

One huge model in miniature shows the story of transportation of the United States Army from 1776 to the present and into the future. It begins with sailing ships and horse-drawn wagons, progresses through various wars and into 1998, when flying jeeps and all manner of jet-propelled aircraft will transport American soldiers.

There is an old tree trunk, 22 inches in diameter, that was completely cut in two by rifle fire at the Battle of Spotsylvania in May, 1864. Bullets are still embedded in the wood.

The plight of the Confederacy may be seen by two pairs of shoes. One pair, worn by a Confederate soldier, has soles made of wood and iron. The other, worn by a Yankee, has soft leather tops and flexible leather soles.

The knee-length black boots worn by General Grant at Appomattox are but a few feet away from a buckskin coat worn by General Custer during the Indian wars, and throughout the hall are relics of the First and the Second World War.

In the Hall of Naval History are relics (some recovered by Mr. Peterson) from the British frigate *Looe*, which sank in 1744.

One case contains the name plate, binnacle and broken wheel of the U.S.S. *Maine*, sunk without warning at Havana on February 15, 1898, with the loss of 260 men.

There is a huge model of the aircraft carrier U.S.S. *Shangri-La*, commissioned in 1944, and another of the battleship *Missouri*, on whose decks the Japanese formally surrendered to end World War II.

In the same case with the *Missouri* is a model of the schooner *Hannah*, which was one of a fleet of seven ships fitted on orders from General Washington "to pick up storeships and transports" near the American coast during the American Revolution. The *Hannah*, which sailed from Beverly, Massachusetts, was the first armed ship to sail under authority of the Continental Congress and was thus the first armed navy vessel of the United States. Built to scale, the model of the *Hannah* shows that she was only a few feet longer than the big guns poking out from the turrets on the giant *Missouri*, a graphic image of the development of naval vessels during the past 200 years.

For those to whom peaceful pursuits have more appeal, the nation's art treasures are attractively displayed and include some unusual items. Almost everyone is familiar with the painting known as "Whistler's Mother," but who knows about "Whistler's Father"?

Chapter 13

Beauty and Several Beasts

ONE OF THE BEST-KNOWN PAINTINGS IN THE WORLD IS "THE Artist's Mother," popularly called "Whistler's Mother" because it was done by James Abbott McNeill Whistler. It is in a museum on the grounds of the Louvre in Paris, France.

Less well known is "The Artist's Father," which frequently inspires words of surprise among visitors to the Freer Gallery of Art, where this painting hangs along with many more of Whistler's works. Many never realized that he did a portrait of his Dad.

The Freer Gallery was established through the generosity of Charles L. Freer of Kingston, New York. While still in his teens Freer worked in a cement factory; a general store; and for the New York, Kingston & Syracuse Railroad, a company in which he carved his future. In 1900, when Freer was only 44 years old, he retired from business and until his death in 1919 he devoted his life to the study and development of his art collections, which he had begun in the early 1880s.

Freer and Whistler were good friends and Freer collected many of Whistler's paintings and etchings. In addition, Freer traveled to Europe, Egypt, India, China, Japan and other countries and centered his interests on Oriental art. He set up an endowment fund in trust to the Smithsonian Institution to provide for the study and acquisition of Oriental fine arts, and upon his death his collection was removed to Washington and placed in a building given by Freer, designed according to his wishes and built on the grounds of the Smithsonian Institution. It was opened to the public on May 2, 1923.

Under the terms of Freer's endowment all works of art in the Freer Gallery are obtained by purchase only, none by loan or gift. Also, the only additions that can be made to the collection are works from the Near or Far East, no others. Most members of the gallery staff speak Japanese and several European languages, and one speaks Persian and writes Arabic.

Art lovers from many countries visit the gallery to see sculpture, pottery, porcelain, glass, manuscripts and metalwork by artists from China, Japan, Korea, India, Iran, Egypt and Syria. Among outstanding ancient Biblical manuscripts are the fourth-and-fifth-century manuscript of the Gospel according to the four Evangelists, and a third-century Greek papyrus of *The Minor Prophets.*

Whistler's works include oils, water colors, pastels, drawings, etchings and lithographs. Other painters represented include George deForest Brush, Childe Hassam, Winslow Homer, Albert Pinkham Ryder and John Singer Sargent, and there are two sculptures by Augustus Saint-Gaudens.

While the gallery is famous for its art works, it also has a magnificent art library of some 44,000 books, pamphlets and periodicals which is open to the public without charge from 9:00 A.M. to 4:30 P.M. daily, Monday through Friday. Some of the books are so huge they are called "elephant size," and they are kept on specially designed shelves that may be pulled out on rollers. The reference materials are available in the library but cannot be borrowed or removed.

A Japanese artisan named Takashi Sugiura is one of the only two craftsmen in the Western world skilled in the mounting and repair or restoration of Oriental paintings, many of which are on silk or fragile paper. In mountings he uses ancient Oriental materials and methods which have been handed down from father to son, for in each mounting he must consider that in years to come a painting may have to be treated or cleaned by some other craftsman. If the painting were mounted with modern adhesives or resins it probably could not be removed without destroying or seriously damaging it.

Cleanliness is important to preservation, and the entire Freer collection is cleaned once or twice a year. There is a constant battle against moths, roaches and other insects, and rodents. It is also inspected regularly to see whether any repair work is needed. The gallery has its own chemical laboratory and cabinet shop.

Only about 1800 of the Freer collection of some 10,000 works are on display. The others are available for study by scholars, artists and historians.

Across the Mall from the Freer Gallery, in the Natural History Museum, the Smithsonian maintains its own National Collection of Fine Arts. While the Freer collection is forever closed to American additions, the National Collection is dedicated to the past, present and future of American art and to developing the work of modern American painters and sculptors.

Mr. Thomas M. Beggs, Director of the National Collection, mentioned one way in which this purpose is accomplished. "We provide exhibit facilities for local, state and national groups," he said. "Last summer Tennessee artists brought their work here for display. Next January we will show New Jersey artists, with others in the months ahead. We invite art associations to take part, and we also try to inspire the living artist by importing exhibitions from abroad that will stimulate new ideas and new techniques."

Occasionally the Smithsonian is asked by the United States Information Agency and the State Department to organize art exhibitions for them, to be shown abroad. This is a task supervised by the Smithsonian's Traveling Exhibition Service, which regularly circulates about a hundred yearly exhibits of paintings, sculptures, textiles and graphic arts. Most of these go to other museums in the United States, with a few to Canada. The art objects shown are usually the property of the artists. For example, one exhibit in Boston, showing the work of New England artists and sculptors, belonged to these art groups but was taken over by the Smithsonian to be shown for one year throughout the country, after which the pieces were returned to the owners. While such an exhibit is in Smithsonian custody the Institution is responsible for insurance, maintenance, crating and shipping.

Some exhibits designed for children rent for less than fifty dollars. Others are rented at higher fees to schools, colleges, art clubs and other organizations or museums.

The National Collection of Fine Arts includes oil and water-color paintings; sculptures in wood, ivory, stone and in gold, silver and other metals; prints and engravings; ceramics, furniture and textiles, including tapestry and lace.

Mr. Beggs gets many inquiries from the public about works of art. One merchant from Alexandria, Virginia, brought in a painting one morning and said he was thinking of buying it for his home. He wanted to know its value. Mr. Beggs, bound by the Smithsonian's policy not to make appraisals, said that it was worth owning. The merchant relayed this comment to the real owner, who then raised his price. The merchant refused to pay it; so the painting was sold to someone else and presented to another museum, where publicity revealed that it was valued at several hundred times the amount for which the Alexandria storekeeper could have bought it.

One man had inherited a painting supposed to be an original Watteau. An analysis of the picture, together with Mr. Beggs's knowledge of Watteau's work, showed that it had been made a hundred years after Watteau stopped painting.

Gifts to the National Collection average about fifty a year, and very limited funds are available for small purchases. A distinguished Smithsonian Art Commission meets annually to decide which gifts shall be accepted, but for lack for space they cannot promise all donors that their gifts will be publicly displayed. In 1958 Congress provided that the National Collection of Fine Arts be transferred to an old building once used as the Patent Office, and when this move is made (probably by 1963) a great many of the paintings and other art objects now in the study collection will be put on display.

The other great art collection in the Smithsonian's realm is in the National Gallery of Art, on Constitution Avenue between 4th and 7th streets, a short distance from the Natural History Museum.

Ernest Feidler, Administrator of the National Gallery, told me that it is probably the largest all-marble structure in the world today—785 feet long, with more than half a million square feet of floor space. It is often called The Mellon Gallery because it was built with funds given by the late Andrew W. Mellon. When he offered the money to the government through President Franklin D. Roosevelt, the President said, "You and I have been political opponents for years, and this is one of the most magnanimous things I've ever heard of. I shall recommend to the Congress that we accept your gift and call it the Mellon Art Gallery."

"No," Mr. Mellon said. "It isn't intended as a memorial. I'm hoping that other people will give important art collections and make contributions to the gallery, but they won't do it just because it has my name. Who would give money to Carnegie Tech, or Harvard, or Yale, for example, simply to perpetuate the names of their founders?"

The building was begun in June, 1937. Before it was completed in December, 1940, Samuel Kress donated his magnificent Italian art collection, and since that time the gallery has acquired the Widener, Chester Dale and Lessing Rosenwald collections, numerous individual masterpieces and gifts of money to buy others. Mellon's own art collection was valued at 50 million dollars.

One day a Chicago attorney asked Mr. Feidler to come to Chicago to discuss a proposed financial gift. In Chicago, Mr. Feidler met the attorney's client, a woman, but her name was not mentioned at the time, and only after she donated $500,-000 to the gallery did he learn that she was Syma Busiel, the original "Lady Esther" of cosmetic fame.

Why did she present the money to the government and not to Chicago, her home? "My fortune and my brother's fortune were made with small amounts of money from people all over the United States," she explained. "I feel that some of it should go back to the people of the United States."

Every year Congress appropriates about $1,800,000 just for the operation and maintenance of the National Gallery, and every year the Congressmen ask how much the art collection is worth. A conservative estimate is that its art treasures are worth more than 250 million dollars, based upon their values when they were acquired. The collection of Rembrandts alone (probably the greatest in the Western Hemisphere) is worth a sizable fortune. There are few places in the world where so many masterpieces are openly displayed where people can come close to them.

Temperature and moisture are carefully controlled day and night. Paintings have pigments which expand and contract at different rates. Heat might make one expand faster than another, causing cracking and flaking in the painting. The air-conditioning system has nine outlets, and in all except one there is filter paper to catch dust. The ninth has a device that attracts dust particles to a plate from which they are later removed. Although there is some dust from footprints of visitors who track in dirt from the street, the National Gallery is probably the cleanest public building in Washington.

There have been few cases of damage. In two or three instances visitors have made fingernail scratches on paintings. Once someone with a warped sense of humor stuck a blob of bubble gum on the painted lips of the figure in Antonio Mor's "Portrait of a Man."

In 1960 the curators answered more than 3000 inquiries of all kinds relating to the gallery and its possessions. They will examine a work of art to determine if it is genuine or what period it represents, but never give appraisals of values.

Many people come to the gallery to make copies of famous paintings. A prospective copyist must show that he is a serious student. The gallery will then supply him with an easel and stool, a canvas sheet to protect the floor from paint, and a private locker in which he may store his materials, all without charge. Many copyists make a living by copying and selling paintings on commission. It takes about two weeks to make a good copy that may sell for $400 or $500. As a precaution, the gallery guards measure all canvases used for copying and make sure that each is noticeably smaller or larger than that of the original.

There are 112 exhibition areas in the gallery, and if a visitor spent five minutes in each one it would take him nine hours to complete his tour, plus time for walking. Most tourists, however, stroll through in an hour or two.

One of the gallery's visitors' aids is the "Lectour," a tiny radio receiver with disposable earpieces (for sanitation). Developed by Frank Mackintosh, who designed a radio system for Thailand, the Lectour permits its holder to hear a description of the art in many of the galleries and thus enjoy it to the fullest. The Lectour rents for 25 cents. For those who do not use it there are free guided tours throughout the day.

The National Gallery, the Freer Gallery, the Natural History Museum and the Museum of History and Technology deal primarily with inanimate objects, but one Smithsonian bureau that is teeming with living things is the National Zoological Park.

My own opinion is that the Washington Zoo is not truly a

"national" zoo, but it certainly ought to be. A "national" zoo would be supported by the federal government. The Washington Zoo, even though it is supposedly a part of the Smithsonian, is operated with funds allotted to it by the government of the District of Columbia—and from my observations it appears that these funds are so limited that sections of the park are deteriorating.

Considering the billions of dollars given to other countries for foreign aid (some of which might be used to improve foreign zoos), it would seem that if we are to have a "National" Zoological Park it should have facilities of which our government and people can be proud. Ironically it does have a fine zoological collection, but the buildings are antiquated, cracking, leaky and deserving of modernization or replacement. Some fences bordering the park would long since have fallen if they were not held up by tangles of honeysuckle vines.

This could and should be one of the finest zoological parks in the country, or even in the world, and I feel sure it would be if Congress provided the necessary money for its improvement.

Even the office of youthful Director Theodore H. Reed is in a rickety old building once known as the Holt mansion. As long ago as 1890 the zoo manager reported that this house was "in a very dilapidated condition." The roof leaks; plaster has fallen from the ceilings; and once when the floor was eaten by termites and caved in, one of the zoo's anteaters was rushed to the rescue to gobble down the termites!

On two panes of one of the original windows in the house are two interesting inscriptions scratched in the glass. One says, "Hurra for Hickory. O. S. Laines, December 12th, 1827." The other reads, "McDonald. Huzza for Adams. Down with Hickory's enemies. Hickory for ever." (Hickory was Andrew Jackson.)

The zoo has about 2500 animals on its 176 acres of wooded land, through which wander some four million visitors a year.

A part of the park was once owned by John Quincy Adams, who built "Adam's Mill" on nearby Rock Creek. Today one area of the park fronts on Adams Mill Road.

One of the zoo's popular attractions is "Smoky the Bear," known to millions of television viewers as the symbol of forest-fire prevention. Smoky was 10 years old in 1960 and weighed 400 pounds, but there was a day when he was not so healthy. In 1950 there was a forest fire in the Capital Mountain area of the Lincoln National Forest in southeastern New Mexico. After it was extinguished a small, badly burned bear cub was found. He was taken to Santa Fe, where his burns were treated and finally healed; then he was presented to the Washington Zoo, where he became a symbol for the Forest Service fire-prevention program.

Many of the animals are gifts from Presidents of the United States, who in turn have received them from foreign dignitaries. This custom started with Theodore Roosevelt, who presented the zoo with two baboons, a lion and an ostrich—all sent to him by Ethiopia's Emperor Menelik.

Two prize specimens are gorillas trapped by three amateur hunters in French Equatorial Africa in 1955. Moka, the 6-year-old female, and Nikumba, the 5½-year-old male, like to throw things at the spectators because they have learned that the crowd will yell and scream, and the animals enjoy the attention. Gorillas in zoos grow as heavy as 600 pounds and may live as long as 40 years; but they are subject to many human ailments, especially tuberculosis, bronchial disorders and common colds. Moka and Nikumba started on a milk formula similar to that for a human baby, supplemented with oranges, bread, sweet potatoes and custard pudding. Now they get three hearty meals a day, along with spoon-fed vitamins. Nikumba delights in grabbing his keeper's hand and running him around the cage, while Moka screams to be picked up and held.

When I talked with Dr. Reed he was preparing to leave for

India to get a rare white tiger, born in 1958 in captivity on the private estate of the Maharajah of Rewa. The tiger was purchased by the Metropolitan Broadcasting Company as a gift to the children of America. It was being held in a big compound, where it was raised with its mother. If its only contact with humans had been in looking at them from a pit, it might be very wild when locked in a cage by itself. Dr. Reed explained that he would use tranquilizing drugs to keep the beast under control while traveling.

Tranquilizers are used in most zoos to calm an animal that needs medical or surgical treatment. A drug is put into a special hypodermic needle that is shot from a "capture gun" outside the cage with enough force to inject the drug into the animal so that it can receive necessary attention.

Feeding the zoo's population requires a knowledge of nutrition. One old theory was that different animals must have different kinds of food, but this does not fit in with nutrition essentials. The fact that a monkey likes to eat some particular morsel doesn't mean that he must live on it. The Philadelphia Zoo worked out a basic diet which Dr. Reed uses for all omnivores (meat-and-vegetable eaters). Basically it is a mixture of grain and meat, supplemented by kale, oranges and other vitamin-rich foods.

The three-toed sloth must have a special dish called "Congo pump," or "mucka-mucka," made from plants grown in the zoo's greenhouses. Dr. Reed and his staff are trying to get the sloth interested in eating food that is more easily obtainable.

Anteaters get a meat mixture with cooked eggs, and with minerals and vitamins added. Their food must be soft because they have no teeth.

Many snakes refuse to eat food unless it is alive. At one time the zoo conducted a feeding experiment with an instrument much like an electric razor. A dead mouse was placed on the mechanism, and when the current was turned on it made the mouse wiggle. The snake, fooled into thinking that the animal was alive, pounced upon and ate it, but this method was discarded because the metal device could damage a snake's fangs. For some of the larger snakes a freshly killed rabbit is put into the cage and made to move with a stick to give the appearance of life. The reason it must be freshly killed is that the snake finds its prey only by the heat in the prey's body, and could not find a cold carcass.

All newly acquired animals are given names by Dr. Reed, who makes sure that every attendant knows what each animal will be called and that no keeper or other employee uses pet names of his own; otherwise the animal will be confused when called, for most of the wild animals will respond to the names they are given. Otto the Potto is a kind of weasel sent here from Africa in 1959. Early in 1960 the zoo received a pigmy hippopotamus from the government of Liberia. The zoo already had three female hippos, all named Gumdrop, and this name had been used for 20 others over the years; so the new arrival was called Totota, after the country estate and zoo of Liberia's President, William V. S. Tubman.

Bongo, a 6000-pound river hippopotamus, was 47 years old when he and his mate, Ricky, were sent to an animal farm in Newmarket, Virginia, to retire. There Bongo developed a foot infection which led to his death, and an autopsy was performed that graphically demonstrated the thoughtlessness and cruelty of some people who visit zoological parks. In Bongo's stomach were found a plastic wallet, a hundred pennies, a nickel, a dime, several pounds of sand and rocks, a lipstick case, a .22-caliber cartridge case, a .38-caliber shell, assorted marbles, pieces of glass and nails and some streetcar tokens, all of which had been tossed down his gaping throat as he pleaded for peanuts from spectators at his enclosure.

Spectators at any zoo must never forget that the animals in the cages are inherently wild beasts, not domestic pets. One tragic episode at the Washington Zoo made this all too clear. In 1958 a two-and-one-half-year-old girl, visiting the zoo with her grandfather, left him and ducked under a barrier in front of a cage housing a lion and lioness. She had a bag of peanuts, some of which she apparently intended to feed to the beasts.

The rest of the story was poignantly told by a 12-year-old boy who was with a school group at another cage in the same building: "I heard a loud scream by the lion's cage," he said. "I ran up to look, and this little girl was in front of the lion cage and the lion had caught her by the leg and was pulling. A man [her grandfather] grabbed her arms and tried to pull her away, but the lion was stronger. He kept pulling and got her body in the cage with him. The man kept hitting the lion on the head trying to make him stop. The lion started walking around inside with her in his mouth, like a rag doll. He was growling. I ran away."

This was the first accident to occur in the lion house since it was built sixty years earlier. It was a terrible tragedy that saddened all those who knew about it, and every precaution has been taken to prevent any recurrence or direct contact between any spectators and the jungle beasts in the various cages.

On the lighter side I asked Dr. Reed about the "April Foolers" who leave messages for friends to call a telephone number (the zoo) and ask for "Mr. Fox," or "Mr. Wolf."

He grinned. "Or Mr. Lyon, or Mr. Bear," he said. "I think one of the best ones was Mr. L. E. Fant. Yes, we got so many calls of that kind that we've made it a policy to discontinue telephone service entirely on April Fool's Day."

There is no day, however, when the zoo is closed to the public. In its 60 years of existence the National Zoological Park has been closed only 2½ days—during one week in the 1930s, when the elephants and rhinoceroses had to be moved from an old house to a new one. There is free parking for more than 1100 cars; there is no admission charge, and you and your friends are always welcome.

The zoo residents are alive and real, and the trees and grass and flowers around them are also living and growing. The animals you see in the Natural History Museum, however, are stuffed; and although the grasses, trees and plants in the display cases may look like the real thing, most of them are man-made in curious ways.

Chapter 14

Backstage Business

IN THE HALL OF MAMMALS IN THE NATURAL HISTORY MUSEUM the mounted specimens are shown against natural backgrounds of trees and grass. The evergreen trees are real and have been preserved with formaldehyde, although their branches have been sprayed with green paint. The trees with leaves, however, are fakes from the ground up! Trunks and limbs are molded of plaster or some other substance; and the realistic leaves are fashioned from cotton and wax and painted green or red or gold, depending upon the seasonal effect desired. In one case, oak leaves were actually cut-out colored photographs of real oak leaves.

The craftsmen who make the exhibit materials are called "preparators," and I talked with Mr. A. Joseph Andrews, a trained sculptor, who is Chief Exhibits Preparator for the Department of Anthropology. In his laboratory are shelves reaching from the floor to the top of the 16-foot ceiling, all filled with plaster molds from which he has made duplicates of countless objects such as spearheads or other weapons, faces from life masks, and pottery.

Mr. Andrews showed me several hats and bowls woven of grass fiber by Indians in Alaska, which came to him to be preserved. As a preservative he melts wax in an ordinary double boiler and mixes it with gasoline on a table under a flue which draws off the fumes. The mixture of gasoline and wax is then rubbed into the fibers; and since the gasoline causes the wax to penetrate, the fibers will last indefinitely. Without this treatment the specimens would gradually deteriorate.

Andrews is an expert in the making of dioramas—three-dimensional miniature models—and many examples of his handiwork are on view in the museum. For a diorama a curator writes a "scenario," telling the story he wants to depict in a display. Andrews then makes a sketch in pencil, followed by a three-dimensional model with paper cutouts. When these are approved by the curator, Andrews actually sculptures figures in the round—four times larger than the paper models. Any archaeological artifacts, such as spears or arrows, must be accurately made in miniature.

His first step in making a figure is to produce a wire armature—something like a child's drawing of a "stick man." Modeling clay is then built up around the wire; and the physical features are carefully shaped, including whatever facial expressions are needed. When the figure is complete it is molded in plaster, which hardens and is separated in two pieces. The clay model is removed, and another wired armature, bound in cotton, is placed in the depressions in the plaster. The plaster sections are put together and molten beeswax is poured into them through a funnel. When the wax cools, the plaster is again opened and there is a wax replica of the original clay model, ready to be painted and installed in the diorama.

To get proper perspective in a diorama, figures of people and animals in the foreground are made larger than those in the background, even though all of the figures are necessarily very close together. With Mr. Andrews I went into the museum and saw a diorama he made, called "Blackfoot Indian Buffalo Drive." It shows how Indians sometimes hunted buffalo by driving the beasts to their death over a cliff. In the Indian Hall he made sketches of buffalo as the basis for his models.

He took measurements from the actual skeleton of a real buffalo to be sure to get correct proportions. To give the effect of a whole thundering buffalo herd he needed four sizes, so his models were made to scales ranging from $3/4'' = 1'$ to $1\frac{1}{2}'' = 1'$. These four sizes give the illusion of distance and perspective in the whole herd.

For miniature tree leaves in dioramas, he etches a copper plate with impressions of tiny leaves and branches. Plastic is poured over the etched plate, hardened and pulled off. Edges are trimmed away and the remaining designs are painted, or sometimes colored plastic is used.

One neat trick he showed me was the making of small realistic background trees from pieces of ordinary sponge, dyed green and cut to shape.

For tree trunks and limbs a wire mold is covered with wax, shaped as desired and colored with artists' oil paints.

For tiny grasses he uses sisal (hemp) or sometimes the bristles from artists' brushes.

His diorama of a Yosemite Indian village was modeled from an actual location in the Yosemite Valley. Indian arrows no bigger than toothpicks are authentic miniature reproductions. Pine-tree needles are sisal. Acorns in a pot and being gathered by Indians are lentils. The foreground grass is real moss preserved with formaldehyde. Grass in the background is sawdust, dyed green. One Indian carries a deerskin, head and all—made of muslin. The bark tepees are really wax, but the spectator can't tell the difference.

No wonder it takes from 8 to 14 months to complete one diorama!

Some "leaves" for full-size trees are produced by making molds using real leaves as patterns. The stem is cut away, into the center of the leaf itself, and a fine wire is tapered by dipping it up and down in acid so that it will fit into the space formerly occupied by the stem. The mold is then used to make wax copies, each of which will have a wire stem by which the leaf can be attached to a branch.

In some of the natural history displays, the blades of green grass were actually scissored out of paper, wax-coated and painted.

One of Mr. Andrews' tasks was to make the life-size figures for displaying the gowns in the First Ladies Hall. Each had to be individually made so that its dress would fit perfectly. The arms were made separately so that the dress could be fitted first; then the arms were put on and the dressing finished.

Contrary to the opinion of many spectators, the face of each of the First Ladies is the same—modeled from the face of Cordelia, a marble bust in the National Collection of Fine Arts. A slight difference is in the eyes, which are modeled because the Cordelia has smooth eyes, without features. The characteristic that makes the First Ladies' faces *seem* different is their hair, which is sculptured to represent the hairdress known to have been worn by each of them.

To learn about the mounting of life-size animals I talked with Watson Perrygo, the taxidermist we met in Chapter 1. Hanging from the ceiling in his laboratory were a peacock tail, a mounted seal made of building paper, Spanish moss, a deer head, two owls and a pheasant. On a table was a spined lizard made of papier-mâché. Along the walls were several stems with large green ferns, all artificial, being made for a new dinosaur display. A post was sticking up out of a vise on a workbench, and around the post the brown trunk of a tree was being fashioned from papier-mâché and sisal. On Mr. Perrygo's desk was the mounted head of an American eagle.

One unusual task was the modeling of a python, patterned after a 305-pound specimen that died in the zoo. A plaster mold was made from the body of the real snake, but the snake-skin was not used because its scales would have a tendency to curl up. Instead, Perrygo and his associates made scales cut from celluloid, painted scale by scale! Most of the snakes in the Smithsonian exhibits have artificial skins, though they look real enough to the viewer.

Mr. Perrygo showed me several specimens that had been made by a new "freeze-dry" method. Preservation of animals by this means was discovered by Dr. Harold T. Meryman of the Naval Medical Research Institute in Bethesda, Maryland, when a cardinal flew into a mousetrap near his home and was killed. Dr. Meryman experimented to see if the bird could be preserved. He froze its legs in a life-like position with liquid nitrogen; then he put the bird into his home freezer, where the moisture in its body turned to ice. Using a vacuum pump and a chemical dryer, he slowly removed the water in the form of vapor, leaving a dehydrated and lifelike cardinal.

A young California zoologist, Jon Gurnee, who has improved upon this technique, has been hired by the Smithsonian to conduct more experiments and to collaborate with Dr. Meryman. The freeze-dry method eliminates the need for skinning and stuffing an animal, but Mr. Perrygo and others feel that taxidermy will continue to play an important part in museum work.

One of the most popular attractions in the Smithsonian is the Fénykövi elephant. W. L. Brown, who was chief taxidermist when the elephant hide was received, is no longer with the Smithsonian, but has described the difficult job of mounting the specimen.

"When the hide arrived at the museum it was in one piece, so it had to be cut into three parts for tanning," Mr. Brown said.

A miniature model was sculptured to an exact scale of two inches for each foot of the life-size specimen, and a wooden armature or frame, two or three inches under life-size, was constructed so that it could be separated into three sections—head and neck, and two body halves. A clay elephant-shaped figure was built around this armature, which had to be supported by four giant A-shaped trusses.

Because the air was very dry in the hall where the work was in progress, a large plastic housing was built around the frame and a steam line was inserted to raise the humidity and keep the clay from drying out.

When the clay model was finished the hide was placed over it, adjusted, and worked on until every wrinkle was restored. Then a plaster-of-paris mold, reinforced with sisal fiber, was placed over each of the sections to hold the skin in exact position. Each mold was strengthened with wooden beams; then the plastic housing was taken down and each of the three plaster sections was lowered to the floor by two two-ton hoists.

Now all inner armature, clay, wire and other superfluous materials were removed, leaving the elephant skin alone attached to the outer plaster mold. When the inner skin had been thoroughly cleaned, a layer of plaster about three-fourths of an inch thick was applied, so that the skin was now between two layers of plaster while drying. When thoroughly dry the inner coating was carefully removed, and three layers of burlap and two layers of aluminum screen wire, each reinforced with papier-mâché, were laminated to the inner hide. This produced a thin manikin, very tough and durable, about half an inch thick.

Next, another internal armature of seasoned wooden ribs was built and fastened to the inside of the manikin for support. At this stage the outer wooden frame and plaster mold were removed, exposing two halves of the elephant skin. The halves were joined together from within by bolting, and papier-mâché was used to cover the seams.

The head was treated the same way, except for support. A wooden structure was made inside the head to hold a long beam by which the head would be supported when attached to the body. The tusks were inserted and the head was fastened to the body halves. After the seams had been sealed, the artificial eyes were installed and the hide was restored to its original color.

When you see the Fénykövi elephant you are really looking at the skin of the original animal which covers a framework made to fit it; but there are no traces of the taxidermists' work, and the great beast looks almost as though it would take its next step at any moment.

The new and modern look in the Smithsonian halls is due in part to the Smithsonian's progressive exhibit staff, headed by John Anglim. When I talked with Mr. Anglim he was hard at work on the exhibit program for the new Museum of History and Technology, surrounded by blueprints of the new building, architects' drawings and plans or models for new exhibits.

In the halls which have already been modernized the descriptive panels and cases were so designed that they may be moved intact to the new building when the time comes. Others will be built from scratch.

New exhibits are prepared on the basis of a script furnished by the curator of whatever division is to be represented. He indicates what specimens he wants to display, and the exhibit specialists decide how the specimens can be shown with the greatest effect.

There are two kinds of designers. The architectural, or hall designer, determines the size and placement of cases and panels, the colors to be used, the kind of textiles, if any, ceiling heights, floor textures and other such characteristics.

The graphic designer, working from the curator's script, designs the cases themselves, placing the emphasis wherever the curator wants it.

The cases are made by outside contractors.

Mr. Anglim and I walked into one huge hall littered with

boards, tarpaulins, tools and paint buckets. On the wall opposite the entrance was the immense head and part of the body of a life-size model of a blue whale. The part of the body not yet reproduced was a framework of wooden ribs which would eventually be covered with the same Fiberglas used for the head. When the covering is complete the wooden "skeleton" will be removed.

The head itself was modeled of Fiberglas on the floor, then lifted into position against the wall. At one point the head slipped forward on the scaffolding with a workman inside, but this modern Jonah in overalls was only slightly bruised and no one was seriously injured.

This blue whale, some 90 feet long, will dominate the Hall of Marine Life, designed to explain many things about the ocean. Visitors will see giant squid and other creatures of the deep and will learn how countless billions of tiny sea animals are used as food for the larger ones. Above various alcoves will be a balcony with four groups showing a typical sandy shore, a rocky shore, a marshy shore and a coral reef. The hall will also have a replica of a South Pacific coral reef.

Care must be taken to keep insects out of cases. Mr. Anglim told me about one case that had been finished and closed up for several weeks. One day a full-grown moth appeared under the glass; and nobody has yet figured out how it could have entered, unless it was present in the larval stage when the case was being made.

Mr. Anglim himself is designing the Hall of Everyday Life in Early America for the new building. This hall will show the development and growth of our country in chronological order as closely as possible, and as we talked in his office I saw some unusual antiques that will probably be used in displays.

One was a "fly trap," a box in which a clock mechanism turns a cloth-covered cylinder. In use the cloth is saturated with syrup or molasses, and flies cling to it as it revolves. They are carried through a slot to the interior of the box, where a horizontal bar scrapes them off the cylinder and into the bottom of the container. This gadget was made about 1875, before the screening of windows became common.

Another device was an apple peeler. An apple is impaled upon sharp prongs. A metal arm with a blade is attached to a spring and placed against the fruit. The user turns a crank which makes the apple revolve as the blade shaves off its skin. This machine will probably be displayed with a wax model of a partly peeled apple.

Most of the design and production work of Mr. Anglim's staff is done at a separate laboratory on 24th Street in Washington, where I talked with his associates, Benjamin Lawless and Bela Bory.

As Mr. Bory explained, "Our job is to furnish a museum. We are its interior decorators."

They have three sections—design, production and a model shop. The work flows in that order, "from designers' two-dimensional dreams to producers' three-dimensional models. All are coordinated with the curators, because we develop the exhibits with and for them," Mr. Bory said.

One object I noticed in the laboratory was a metal framework about 12 feet high supporting a rather small rocket. This turned out to be the original frame for one of the early rockets of Dr. Robert Goddard, American space pioneer, although the rocket shown with it was made in the shop from photographs of the original.

Dr. Goddard was experimenting with rockets before and after World War I. One of the last rockets on which he worked is shown in the Air Museum and is remarkably like the German V-2 weapons that blasted London with such damaging effect in World War II. It is said that Wernher von Braun, the German rocket expert now active in the United States space program, once remarked about Goddard, "He was far ahead of his time. He had it all."

Among other handiwork of Mr. Anglim's model-makers I saw a miniature reproduction of a Civil War seacoast defense cannon. It is about seven inches long, perfect in every detail, and could be fired successfully. It was made to scale from actual artillery drawings of the original gun.

Another specimen was a model of a 24-pounder (cannon) used on the U.S.S. *Constitution*. It actually has been fired.

In my behind-the-scenes exploration of the Smithsonian I talked with Helena M. Weiss, attractive Registrar of the National Museum. Miss Weiss's office receives and controls all mail, incoming and outgoing, and refers letters to proper curators for reply. She receives any specimens sent to the museum, makes a record of them and refers them to the necessary division for processing. She handles all shipments for the Smithsonian, foreign and domestic; does required work with the Customs Bureau and acts as a liaison with the State Department for passports and visas for Smithsonian scientists who travel abroad.

Some of the mail that comes through her office is rather rib-tickling. One box came in with a pair of shoes on which the soles were worn completely through, the uppers torn and the heels worn away. An accompanying note said, "My friends tell me these are something a museum should have."

One woman sent in a T-shirt riddled with holes, and a letter reading, "My husband insists that the only way I can stop him from wearing this shirt is to send it to a museum."

Another woman sent a letter with a box used for wooden safety matches. The letter said, "Enclosed is a bug I found in my house. What kind is it?" Unfortunately she had cut holes in the matchbox to provide air for the bug, and by the time the box arrived the bug had departed.

"Our most frequent inquiries are from people asking about Stradivarius violins," Miss Weiss told me. "A great many think they have genuine Stradivari when they really have fakes. There are so many questions on this subject that we have prepared a printed leaflet to save time in replying."

Young men and women trying to earn a doctorate in college sometimes write to the Smithsonian on various subjects, hoping that the Institution will send them replies detailed enough to be submitted as their own theses!

Whenever there is newspaper or magazine publicity on some particular subject related to the work of the Smithsonian, a flood of letters comes in. One magazine published a story called "Gold in Your Own Back Yard," which indicated that certain kinds of gravel might contain gold dust. The Smithsonian was promptly smothered with *tons* of gravel from hundreds of people who wanted to get rich quick. None was valuable, and the Smithsonian called it "back yard gravel." They asked senders to send money for return postage if they wanted the gravel back; and most of them did so, perhaps refusing to believe that the stuff was worthless.

While the public displays in the Smithsonian have great educational value, the *real* "diffusion of knowledge" by the Institution is accomplished through its many publications. The first Smithsonian publication, entitled *Ancient Monuments of the Mississippi Valley*, was produced in 1848. Since that time millions of copies of pamphlets and books have been distributed free to libraries and scientific institutions and to individual scientists and scholars throughout the world.

The publications represent the various branches of science, including anthropology, ethnology and archaeology, botany, zoology, mechanics and aeronautics, physics, chemistry, geology, astronomy, meteorology, physiology and numerous other subjects. Most are of a technical nature, not readily understandable by laymen. Some, of course, are for popular consumption.

During World War II a special Smithsonian series called

"War Background Studies" attracted wide attention. These were illustrated booklets on the peoples, history, geography and other features of far-flung parts of the earth to which the war reached, especially in the Pacific.

Smithsonian publications which are paid for from the Smithsonian's government appropriation for printing can be bought only from the Superintendent of Documents, Government Printing Office, Washington 25, D.C. The Smithsonian has a limited number of these publications which it furnishes without charge to scientists and scholars not on the regular distribution lists who need them for special research projects.

Some publications, including most of those sold at the information desks in the museum buildings, are paid for with private funds which have been given to the Smithsonian, and are for public sale. Copies of these publications, however, also go without charge to many scientific institutions and libraries all over the world.

Before I finished at the Smithsonian, I visited Captain W. B. Stiles of the Smithsonian Guard Force, to ask what he and his men believed were the most popular of the museum exhibits.

"I think the most popular in History and Technology is the *Spirit of St. Louis*, followed by the First Ladies' Hall and the missiles and rockets," Captain Stiles said. "In the Natural History Museum the big elephant and the Hope Diamond attract most attention. Some kids get so excited about the elephant when they first see it that they run into and knock down the rope barrier around it. The other day I heard one six-year-old tell his mother, 'Look, Mommy, it's even bigger than Daddy!' "

Another exhibit very popular with boys and girls is the display of shrunken heads! "They all go back home and tell their friends about it," Captain Stiles said. "The guards are constantly being asked where it is."

"People are interested in queer things," he added. "Once we had on display an exhibit of skins, including a pair of boots made of human skin taken from the back of a prisoner who had died in New York State. The drivers of the sightseeing buses always told their passengers to be sure and ask the guards to show them the skin boots. This exhibit was changed after World War II, but for the next ten years scores of people still asked about it."

Occasionally youngsters play hooky from school to visit the Smithsonian. One was found out when he approached a mounted lion's head set on a pedestal. The boy stuck his hand in the lion's mouth and couldn't get it out. He pulled so hard the pedestal came forward and the head toppled to the floor, still holding the boy's hand. He cried out; a guard rushed in and extricated the hand; but the lad was so frightened he could neither walk nor talk and the guard carried him to the office, where he stayed until he returned to normal—and to school.

So far as I know there has been only one thing in the Smithsonian that eluded both a visitor and a guard. The guard was brand-new, nervous and not well educated. The visitor was a lady who came up to him in one of the halls and said, "Excuse me, but can you tell me where the exit is?"

He scratched his chin and said, "I'm sorry, lady, but you'd better try the building across the Mall. There's a lot of stuff over there!"

Whether you are looking for the exit or for airplanes or guns or monkeys or lions or Indians or jewelry, or toys or paintings or sculptures or practically anything else you can think of, the chances are that you will find it in the Smithsonian. People who first visited this wonderful place as children are now bringing their own children and even their grandchildren to see the sights. The Smithsonian belongs to them and to you and to all of the people of the United States, and it has something to make every American proud, or happy, or thoughtful, or perhaps wiser than he was when he walked into this amazing storehouse of so many millions of treasures.

Certainly James Smithson would agree that the Smithsonian has amply fulfilled his dream of an Institution dedicated to the "increase and diffusion of knowledge among men."

WHERE TO GO
and
WHAT TO SEE

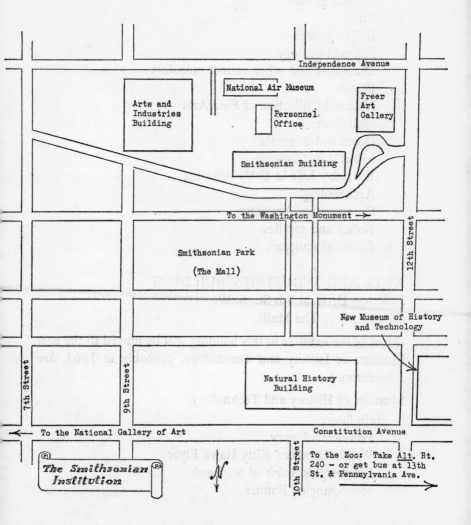

Independence Avenue

National Air Museum

Arts and Industries Building

Personnel Office

Freer Art Gallery

Smithsonian Building

To the Washington Monument →

Smithsonian Park

(The Mall)

12th Street

New Museum of History and Technology

7th Street

9th Street

Natural History Building

To the National Gallery of Art ←

Constitution Avenue

10th Street

The Smithsonian Institution

To the Zoo: Take Alt. Rt. 240 - or get bus at 13th St. & Pennsylvania Ave.

NATURAL HISTORY BUILDING
Constitution Ave. at 10th St., N. W.
(North side of The Mall)

Ground floor:
    Changing exhibits; auditorium; rest rooms
First floor:
    Animal groups
    Birds
    Indian groups
    Physical geology
    Dinosaurs and other extinct monsters
    Fossils
    National Collection of Fine Arts
Second floor:
    Gems and minerals
    Musical instruments
    Everyday Life in Early America
    Archaeology
    Comparative Anatomy
    Fishes and reptiles
    Classical sculpture

ARTS AND INDUSTRIES BUILDING
Jefferson Drive at 9th St., S. W.
(South side of The Mall)

(Most of the exhibits in this building will be moved to the new
Museum of History and Technology, probably in 1963. *See
later listing.*)

Museum of History and Technology
    Main floor:
        Power machinery
        Wright Brothers' Kitty Hawk Flyer
        Lindbergh's *Spirit of St. Louis*
        Star-Spangled Banner

Hall of Military History
Hall of Naval History
First Ladies' Hall
Coin collection
Stamp collection
Hall of Civil History
Hall of Transportation
Hall of Textiles
Farm machinery
Aeronautics (Several aeronautical displays are here for
    lack of space in the Air Museum.)
Gallery:
Ceramics
Photography
Medicine, Pharmacy, Apothecary Shop
Hall of Health
Weapons
Military Uniforms
Typewriters, clocks, watches, light machinery
Textiles
Working beehive

SMITHSONIAN BUILDING
Jefferson Drive at 10th St., S. W.
(South side of The Mall)
(Entrance north door, under tower)

Index exhibit of Smithsonian activities
Hall of Graphic Arts
Tomb of James Smithson

NATIONAL AIR MUSEUM
Gray steel hangar, south of Smithsonian brownstone building

Famous aircraft
Rocket nose cones
History of flight

FREER GALLERY OF ART
Jefferson Drive at 12th St., S. W.
(South side of The Mall)

>Oriental art
>Paintings by Whistler, Sargent, Homer
>Ancient Biblical manuscripts

NATIONAL GALLERY OF ART
Constitution Ave. at 6th St., N. W.

>Art collections of Mellon, Kress, Widener, Dale, Rosen-
>   wald and others
>Paintings and sculptures

NATIONAL ZOOLOGICAL PARK
Rock Creek Park.
(Entrance: 3000-block of Connecticut Ave.; also by way of
Harvard Street or Adams Mill Road, N. W.)

>Animals, birds, reptiles

(NEW) MUSEUM OF HISTORY AND TECHNOLOGY
(Scheduled opening, 1963)
Constitution Ave. at 12th St., N. W.

The following guide is based upon architectural plans for
the new building as of 1961:

>First floor:
>   Information desk; checkrooms; directory of special ex-
>   hibits
>   Agricultural implements and machinery
>   Wood and wood products
>   Watercraft
>   Automobiles, coaches, locomotives
>   Models of bridge and tunnel construction
>   Power machinery

Electronics
Typewriters, clocks, light machinery
Tools
Astronomical instruments
Chemical apparatus
Medical, pharmaceutical, dental instruments
Textiles, textile machinery
Nuclear energy exhibits
Petroleum production

Second floor:
Star-Spangled Banner
History of the United States, including:
Weapons
Tools
Architecture
Home interiors
American costume and dress
First Ladies' gowns
Personal memorabilia
(Washington, Lincoln and others)

Third floor:
Weapons, flags, uniforms, insignia
Warship models
Prints, maps, etc., illustrating history of the Armed
Forces of the United States
Musical instruments
Printing equipment and prints
Photography
Ceramics and glass
Coin collection (History of money)
Stamp collection (History of the mails)

Fourth and fifth floors:
Reserve collections of textiles, silver, coins, clocks,
watches, patent models, glass, scientific instruments,

ceramics, tools, etc., organized for efficient reference
for use of historians, writers and serious hobbyists.
Workrooms for staff.
Study rooms for visiting inventors, scientists, engineers
and historians.
Basement:
Public Cafeteria
Mining industry exhibits

HOURS: All buildings except the National Gallery of Art are
open from 9:00 A.M. to 4:30 P.M. weekdays and Sundays. The
National Gallery is open from 10:00 A.M. to 5:00 P.M. weekdays, 2:00 P.M. to 10:00 P.M. Sundays. The zoo buildings are
open from 9:00 A.M. to 5:30 P.M. in summer, to 4:30 P.M. in
winter. The zoo *grounds* are open from 9:00 A.M. to dusk
every day.

Index

069
N

Neal, Harry Edward
Treasures by the Millions